ADVANCES IN REPRODUCTIVE TECHNOLOGY RESEARCH

HUMAN REPRODUCTIVE SYSTEM - ANATOMY, ROLES AND DISORDERS

Additional books in this series can be found on Nova's website under the Series tab.

Additional e-books in this series can be found on Nova's website under the e-book tab.

HUMAN REPRODUCTIVE SYSTEM - ANATOMY, ROLES AND DISORDERS

ADVANCES IN REPRODUCTIVE TECHNOLOGY RESEARCH

IGNATZ SANGER
EDITOR

New York

For permission to use material from this book please contact us:
Telephone 631-231-7269; Fax 631-231-8175
Web Site: http://www.novapublishers.com

NOTICE TO THE READER

Library of Congress Cataloging-in-Publication Data

ISBN: 978-1-62417-875-7

Library of Congress Control Number: 2012956341

Published by Nova Science Publishers, Inc. † New York

CONTENTS

PREFACE

Assisted reproductive technology (ART) now accounts for 1-3% of all live births in the western world. Several procedures that may be used in the ART process are hormonal stimulation, egg retrieval, in vitro fertilization (IVF), intra-cytoplasmic sperm injection, micro-manipulation of gametes; and exposure to culture medium. Although these techniques are considered safe, in recent years evidence has been accumulating that ART may be associated with an increased risk of birth defects, low birth weight, and genetic imprinting disorders. This book provides current research in reproductive technology with a focus on Down's Syndrome screening in assisted conception pregnancies; sexed semen technology in buffalo breeding and reproductive technologies; a nationwide study of assisted reproductive technology and multiple births and accompanied birth defects; and assisted reproductive technologies and the risk for autism spectrum disorder.

Chapter 1 - The effect of assisted reproductive technology (ART) and non-ART ovulation stimulation fertility treatment on the number and rate of multiple live births from 1974-2011 in Japan was estimated using vital statics and ART statistics. The number of non-ART iatrogenic multiple births was estimated by subtracting the ART multiples from the total iatrogenic multiples, estimated by vital statistics, assuming that spontaneous multiple-birth rates according to maternal age class would be constant. There was an overall increase in the non-ART multiple births during the thirty-year period, whereas ART multiples tended to increase from 1983 to 2005, and then rapidly decreased thereafter. The number or percentage of ART multiples was almost consistently lower than that of non-ART multiples.

Next, a reverse sigmoid curve was assumed and examined using nationwide data associated with single embryo transfers (SET) from 2007 to

2010 in Japan. The multiple pregnancy rates decreased almost linearly when the SET pregnancy rate was between about 40% and 80% of the regression approximation. The linear approximation overestimated multiple pregnancy rates in an early period and underestimated multiple pregnancy rates in the final period. The multiple pregnancy rate seemed to be influenced by the improvement of the total pregnancy rate of ART in the early period and by the MZ twinning after a SET in the final period. The estimated MZ twinning rate after the SET was around 2%.

Moreover, the relationship between ART and birth defects according to plurality was analyzed. The above ART data includes information on birth defects from 2004 to 2010. There were a total of 219,185 pregnancies after ART. The relative risk (RR) and 95% confidence interval (CI) for birth defect categories according to the International Classification of Disease, 10th edition were calculated with singletons as the reference group. Then, recurrence risk ratios (RRRs), which were defined as the probandwise concordance rates of birth defects in twins divided by the prevalence of birth defects in the general population, were calculated as indicators of familial aggregation. In multiples compared to singletons, the percentage of pregnancies with any birth defects per 10,000 pregnancies was significantly higher (RR=1.70, 95% CI 1.50-1.93), the percentage of birth defects per live births was not significantly higher (RR=0.92, 95% CI 0.81-1.05). The most common birth defects of major classification were congenital malformations of the circulatory system for both singletons and multiples. RRs per pregnancy were significant for seven out of the eleven main categories. There were 278 twin pairs, comprised of 14 concordant and 264 discordant pairs, with any birth defects.

Regarding major organ system classification, high probandwise concordance rates were observed for the following: congenital malformations of eye, ear, face, and neck (11.1%), chromosomal abnormalities not elsewhere classified (10.3%), congenital malformations of the circulatory system (9.3%), cleft lip and cleft palate (8.7%), and congenital malformations of the nervous system (8.3%). High RRRs were observed for the following: congenital malformations of the eye, ear, face and neck (RRR=218, 95%; CI 58-815), specifically other congenital malformations of the ear (RRR=425, 95%; CI 117-1547); congenital malformations of the great arteries (RRR=203, 95%; CI 79-519), specifically those of the patent ductus arteriosus (RRR=445, 95%; CI 176-1130); and cleft lip and cleft palate (RRR=149, 95%; CI 39-564), specifically cleft palate with cleft lip (RRR=499, 95%; CI 135-1840). The probandwise concordance rate of any birth defect (9.6%) was nearly the same as the approximated recurrence risk of first-degree relatives (9.0%), which assumed multifactorial inheritance. Some subcategories or individual diseases were more common in multiples compared to singletons. Familial aggregation was also suggested in some birth defects.

Chapter 2 - Over the last three decades, prenatal screening for Down's syndrome (DS) has become an integrated part of antenatal care in most developed countries. In the second trimester, the most common markers are maternal serum human chorionic gonadotrophin (hCG) or its free β-subunit (Fβ-hCG), alpha-fetoprotein (AFP), and unconjugated estriol (uE₃). Large studies using combinations of hCG or Fβ-hCG and either or both of the other markers have confirmed model predictions that about two-thirds of DS-affected pregnancies can be detected with a false positive rate (FPR) of about 5%. The most recent addition to the second trimester serum markers has been Inhibin-A, which is found at higher levels in affected pregnancies. This combination of markers (the "quadruple test") allows the detection of ~75% of DS-affected pregnancies with a FPR of ~5% if gestational age is based on an ultrasound scan.

It is presently accepted that ultrasound can identify and measure subcutaneous fluid collections between the soft tissue covering the fetal spine and the overlying skin during the late first trimester. The thickness of this hypoechoic ultrasonographic feature, defined as nuchal translucency (NT), is associated with chromosomal abnormalities, cardiac and other structural defects, as well as an increased risk of spontaneous abortion. In the first trimester, the combination of maternal serum pregnancy-associated placental protein-A (PAPP-A) and Fβ-hCG can achieve a detection rate of ~60% with a FPR of ~5%.

Combining NT with the above first trimester biochemical serum markers resulted in a combined screening test. It has been reported that such a combination may allow about an 85% DS detection rate with a 5% FPR, a significant improvement of other DS screening tests. Later on, a model of an integrated screening for DS was proposed, which was based on combination of first trimester NT measurement and serum PAPP-A levels with second trimester AFP, β-hCG, E₃ and inhibin. The integrated test could allow a 90% DS detection rate for a 1% FPR.

Another sonographic marker which can be used both in the first and a second trimester in order to improve the prediction of DS is nasal bone (NB) evaluation. Cicero and colleagues found that absence of the NB during first trimester sonography was associated with trisomy 21. The authors estimated that if NB assessment were combined with maternal age and NT measurement, 93% of DS cases would be detected at a 5% false-positive rate and that 85% of cases would still be detected if the false-positive rate were set at 1%. In subsequent studies, the same investigators found that an absent NB was also associated with trisomy 18, trisomy 13, and monosomy X. These data suggest that in high-risk pregnancies, NB assessment is a sensitive and highly specific marker and could be a useful adjunct to NT and serum biochemistry.

In addition to increased NT and absence NB, chromosomal abnormalities are associated with a pattern of characteristic sonographic findings in the first trimester. Trisomy 21 was found to be associated with reverse flow pattern in the ductus venosus, tricuspid regurgitation and maxillary hypoplasia. Although first trimester sonographic markers are potentially the best, some concerns have arisen about their clinical application. Pitfalls may be due to inability to examine the markers, incorrect assessment, or incorrect interpretation of the findings.

It is well known that the maternal serum concentrations of placental and fetal proteins may be affected by various conditions, such as diabetes mellitus, maternal smoking, multiple gestation, ethnic subgroups and wrong dates. Therefore, adjustment criteria were introduced to correct the FPR and the detection rate (DR), thus providing a more accurate patient-specific calculated risk.

Over the past decade, the wide use of various assisted reproduction technologies (ARTs) have risen dramatically. Women who conceived following ART have thus far received the same antenatal screening approach as those who conceived spontaneously. This policy would appear to be inadequate since women who conceived following ART treatment are generally older than are women with spontaneously conceived pregnancies, and are therefore at higher risk for a chromosomal disorder (primarily trisomy 21). Fetuses conceived after intracytoplasmic sperm injection (ICSI) are also known to have an increased risk of chromosomal aberrations. In addition, these women may suffer from various underlying metabolic, endocrinological or genetic diseases, for which ART has been indicated in the first place. Taken together, these factors may lead to overuse of invasive cytogenetic testing and thus may contribute to the 20% amniocentesis rate in pregnant women who conceived with ART. Besides the risk of miscarriage following an invasive procedure, 'high risk' results are associated with emotional sequelae as they raise the anxiety level throughout the process of counseling, invasive procedure and until a reassuring result is received.

The current chapter aims to explore the challenging issue of antenatal DS screening in pregnancies resulting from ART (high order multiple gestations, twins, and singletons). The implication and the management in the attempt to achieve the best evaluation of DS risk for every type of gestation will be discussed.

Chapter 3 - Sexed semen technology has been proved feasible in a number of animal species and in cattle breeding, has especially found economically viable application. In less than 10 years, the same technology has been put to the test in the buffalo species, following detection of buffalo sex chromosomes by fluorescence in situ hybridization (FISH) by using specific X- and Y- probe set derived from flow sorted yak chromosomes, therefore showing the evolutionary conservation of such locus in the water buffalo chromosomes. Considering that in the buffaloes, natural mating is still worldwide the most commonly used strategy adopted for breeding, it is extraordinary that in a relatively short period of time the adoption of sexed semen technology in the same species has given such powerful evidence of efficiency and applicability under farm conditions. Despite the lack of long time selection of bulls for semen selection and freazibility in this species, in recent years some pedigree bulls have been identified and properly selected for semen characteristics and quality. This has led to the first indisputable evidence and effectiveness of the sexed semen technology in buffaloes through AI, in the year 2004. Within the same study, purity of sorted semen (X-bearing spermatozoa) was found to be similar to what already reported in cattle, and pregnancy rates following deposition of reduced concentration of sexed semen (4×10^6) near the utero-tubal junction through use of a special catheter, were reported similar to rates derived from the use of unsorted semen at full dose in similar animals. Subsequently and more recently, both nulliparous and pluriparous buffaloes have been used for AI with an even lower concentration of sexed semen (2×10^6), reporting satisfying pregnancy rates similar to those derived from animals following use of unsorted semen. More importantly, in these last trials, deposition of sexed semen has been carried out without the need of special uterine catheters, but rather with a conventional AI gun by emptying the straw at the very beginning of the uterine horn ispilateral to the ovary bearing the preovulatory follicle. More recently, similar satisfying results from the use of sexed semen through AI have been reported in Murrah and Nili Ravi buffaloes too. Furthermore, in the same latter breeds of river buffaloes, sexed spermatozoa have been used and included into in vitro fertilization procedures, giving rise to developing blastocysts and calves born following transfer into selected and synchronized recipients. The evidence provided from the above mentioned studies are of strong encouragement for further research and wider field application of the sexed semen technology in the buffalo species.

Chapter 4 - The current estimated prevalence of autism spectrum disorder (ASD) is approximately 1:100-150, which reflects a 15-fold increase from studies published a half-century ago. The exact cause of ASD is still unknown and it is now believed that, despite the strong genetic origin, environmental factors may modulate phenotypical expression. Pre-and perinatal events are now the focus of research into risk factors for ASD. Assisted reproductive technology (ART) now accounts for 1-3% of all live births in the western world. Several procedures that may be used in the ART process, such as hormonal stimulation, egg retrieval, *in vitro* fertilization (IVF), intra-cytoplasmic sperm injection (ICSI), micro-manipulation of gametes and exposure to culture medium, could subject the gametes and early embryos to environmental stress. Although these techniques are considered safe, in recent years evidence has been accumulating that ART may be associated with an increased risk of birth defects, low birth weight (LBW), and genetic imprinting disorders. Children arising from ART are also at higher risk for epigenetic and imprinted disorders. Epigenetics refers to heritable modifications of DNA that do not alter the underlying sequence. DNA methylation and histone modification are examples of epigenetic modifications that may lead to imprinting disorders. The majority of evidence regarding the effect of ART on imprinting involves DNA methylation. A possible association between the increase in ART procedures and the increase in ASD prevalence has been investigated. Previous studies have reported conflicting results concerning the association between assisted conception and the risk for ASD. This chapter will address the recent literature on the association between the use of hormonal induction and/or assisted reproductive technologies and the risk for autism. Possible contributing mechanisms will be discussed.

In: Advances in Reproductive Technology ...   ISBN: 978-1-62417-875-7
Editor: Ignatz Sanger   © 2013 Nova Science Publishers, Inc.

Chapter 1

NATIONWIDE STUDY OF ASSISTED REPRODUCTIVE TECHNOLOGY AND MULTIPLE BIRTHS WITH ACCOMPANIED BIRTH DEFECTS

*Syuichi Ooki**

Ishikawa Prefectural Nursing University, Ishikawa, Japan

ABSTRACT

The effect of assisted reproductive technology (ART) and non-ART ovulation stimulation fertility treatment on the number and rate of multiple live births from 1974-2011 in Japan was estimated using vital statics and ART statistics. The number of non-ART iatrogenic multiple births was estimated by subtracting the ART multiples from the total iatrogenic multiples, estimated by vital statistics, assuming that spontaneous multiple-birth rates according to maternal age class would be constant. There was an overall increase in the non-ART multiple births during the thirty-year period, whereas ART multiples tended to increase from 1983 to 2005, and then rapidly decreased thereafter. The number or percentage of ART multiples was almost consistently lower than that of non-ART multiples.

Next, a reverse sigmoid curve was assumed and examined using nationwide data associated with single embryo transfers (SET) from 2007

---

* E-mail: sooki@ishikawa-nu.ac.jp.

to 2010 in Japan. The multiple pregnancy rates decreased almost linearly when the SET pregnancy rate was between about 40% and 80% of the regression approximation. The linear approximation overestimated multiple pregnancy rates in an early period and underestimated multiple pregnancy rates in the final period. The multiple pregnancy rate seemed to be influenced by the improvement of the total pregnancy rate of ART in the early period and by the MZ twinning after a SET in the final period. The estimated MZ twinning rate after the SET was around 2%.

Moreover, the relationship between ART and birth defects according to plurality was analyzed. The above ART data includes information on birth defects from 2004 to 2010. There were a total of 219,185 pregnancies after ART. The relative risk (RR) and 95% confidence interval (CI) for birth defect categories according to the International Classification of Disease, 10th edition were calculated with singletons as the reference group. Then, recurrence risk ratios (RRRs), which were defined as the probandwise concordance rates of birth defects in twins divided by the prevalence of birth defects in the general population, were calculated as indicators of familial aggregation. In multiples compared to singletons, the percentage of pregnancies with any birth defects per 10,000 pregnancies was significantly higher (RR=1.70, 95% CI 1.50-1.93), the percentage of birth defects per live births was not significantly higher (RR=0.92, 95% CI 0.81-1.05). The most common birth defects of major classification were congenital malformations of the circulatory system for both singletons and multiples. RRs per pregnancy were significant for seven out of the eleven main categories. There were 278 twin pairs, comprised of 14 concordant and 264 discordant pairs, with any birth defects.

Regarding major organ system classification, high probandwise concordance rates were observed for the following: congenital malformations of eye, ear, face, and neck (11.1%), chromosomal abnormalities not elsewhere classified (10.3%), congenital malformations of the circulatory system (9.3%), cleft lip and cleft palate (8.7%), and congenital malformations of the nervous system (8.3%). High RRRs were observed for the following: congenital malformations of the eye, ear, face and neck (RRR=218, 95%; CI 58-815), specifically other congenital malformations of the ear (RRR=425, 95%; CI 117-1547); congenital malformations of the great arteries (RRR=203, 95%; CI 79-519), specifically those of the patent ductus arteriosus (RRR=445, 95%; CI 176-1130); and cleft lip and cleft palate (RRR=149, 95%; CI 39-564), specifically cleft palate with cleft lip (RRR=499, 95%; CI 135-1840). The probandwise concordance rate of any birth defect (9.6%) was nearly the same as the approximated recurrence risk of first-degree relatives (9.0%), which assumed multifactorial inheritance. Some subcategories or individual diseases were more common in multiples compared to singletons. Familial aggregation was also suggested in some birth defects.

PART 1. ESTIMATION OF THE CONTRIBUTION OF MATERNAL AGE AND ASSISTED/NON-ASSISTED REPRODUCTIVE TECHNOLOGICAL FERTILITY TREATMENTS ON MULTIPLE BIRTHS DURING THE LAST THIRTY YEARS IN JAPAN: 1974-2011

Introduction

Secular trends associated with the multiple-birth rate in Japan have been described in detail elsewhere (Ooki, 2010a). The author will only touch on them briefly here. The multiple-birth rate is defined as the proportion of all live multiple births per 1,000 live births. According to this definition, the multiple-birth rate was nearly constant between 1951 and1976 (10.4-11.4), as shown in Figure 1. The values for these years in Japan can be regarded as spontaneous multiple-birth rates. The rate gradually increased to 12.4 in 1986, then increased rapidly, peaking in 2005 at 22.7, nearly double the spontaneous multiple-birth rate. The multiple-birth rate has decreased over the past six years (2006-2011) to 18.7 (2011), especially that of triplets/+, suggesting the effect of the single embryo transfer (SET) policy for assisted reproductive technologies (ART). According to the Japanese ART and vital statistics, the percentage of total ART live births increased linearly from 0.22% (2,626/1,208,989) in 1992 to 1.64% (18,168/1,110,721) in 2004 to 2.70% (28,945/1,071,304) in 2010. Thus, the use of ART is becoming widespread in Japan.

Many factors affect spontaneous multiple-birth rates. Of them, well established factors are ethnicity, heredity, maternal age and parity (Bortolus et al., 1999; Bulmer, 1959; Fuster et al., 2008; Hoekstra et al., 2008; Nylander, 1981). These effects are applied exclusively to dizygotic twinning. It is also a well-established fact that the occurrence of spontaneous multiple births increases with advanced maternal age up to the latter half of the 30s, and with increased parity. Numerous studies have shown that increasing use of fertility treatments, both ART and non-ART ovulation stimulation, and increasing maternal age have resulted in an increase of multiple births in developed counties worldwide (Corchia et al., 1996; Derom et al., 1993; Fauser et al., 2005; Kaprio and Marttila, 2005; Macfarlane and Blondel, 2005; Martin et al., 2007; Schieve et al., 2009; Tandberg et al., 2007). However, this phenomenon has become complicated in most developed countries, because this age range coincides with the target age class associated with fertility treatments.

The high multiple-gestation and multiple-birth rates associated with both treatment types tend to induce adverse sequelae, including markedly higher risks of pregnancy complications, preterm delivery, infant death, birth defects, and neurological impairments in survivors of multiple births compared to singletons (Boulet et al., 2008; MacDorman et al., 2005; Pharoah, 2002). Considering the adverse outcomes related to multiple births, the establishment of proper guidelines and monitoring systems is essential (Jones, 2007). As a result, many countries have implemented nationwide registry systems for ART (Tandberg et al., 2007; Wright et al., 2008) and adopted SET policies, thereby lowering the multiple birth rate (Hamberger et al., 2005; Ooki, 2012a). On the other hand, there is insufficient epidemiologic information on non-ART ovulation stimulation (Fauser et al., 2005).

Estimating the numbers or rates of non-ART singletons is very difficult since the total number of, specifically non-ART, fertility treatments is generally unknown (Schieve et al., 2009). However, it is possible to estimate the numbers or rates of iatrogenic or non-ART multiples under several conditions, as will be discussed later.

SET, recently more specifically elective SET (eSET), has been recommended to reduce multiple pregnancies in ART (Coetsier and Dhont, 1998; Gelbaya et al., 2010; Scotland et al., 2011; Van Royen et al., 1999), and many developed countries have adopted this practice, although it is not known exactly when the use of SET began to spread. The effectiveness and technique of SET have been improved in recent years.

Many findings have been accumulated that demonstrate that the use of SET dramatically decreases the twinning rate without lowering pregnancy rates (Kresowik et al., 2011; Milne et al., 2010; Ooki, 2012a). The guideline of the Japan Society of Obstetrics and Gynecology (JSOG) for ART in 1996 stated that embryo transfer should be limited to three, while the 2008 guidelines specified SET in principle. The secular trend of multiples (Figure 1) probably reflects the changes in the JSOG guidelines. There are many studies that have examined the effect of SET on the multiple pregnancy rate (Coetsier and Dhont, 1998; Gelbaya et al., 2010; Kresowik et al., 2011; Milne et al., 2010; Scotland et al., 2011; Van Royen et al., 1999); however, most results have been based on cross-sectional single- and multi-year data.

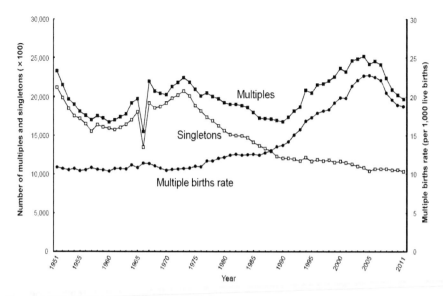

Figure 1. Secular trend of number of live births singletons and multiples and the multiple births rates.

Given this background, the purpose of the present study was first to separate the effects of fertility treatment and of maternal age on the multiple-birth rate indirectly; and second to estimate the effect of ART and non-ART ovulation stimulation fertility treatments on the number and rate of multiple live births during the last thirty years in Japan; and third to examine the theoretical aspect of the effect of SET on the reduction of the multiple pregnancy rate indirectly using two independent data sources, vital statics and ART statistics, which cannot be directly linked, by adding updated data to those of previous studies (Ooki, 2011a, 2011b, 2012a).

Methods

1. Dataset

1) Outline of Japanese Vital Statistics of Multiple Births
All available vital statistics on multiple births within the entire Japanese population between 1974 and 2011, originally collected by the Ministry of Health, Labour and Welfare, were gathered, combined and re-analyzed.

The vital statistics are based on birth records, which are published as an annual report of aggregate, not individual, data. Concerning maternal age, the number of all registered live births were obtained according to plurality (singletons or multiples) and maternal age strata. Maternal age classes were divided into the following six categories; ≤19, 20-24, 25-29, 30-34, 35-39, and ≥40 years. Although the percentage of neonates born to mothers under 20 years and 40 years or more are too small (at most 1% and 4%, respectively), this data was also used for following statistical analyses.

This study defined the rate of multiple births as the proportion of all live multiple births per 1,000 live births. As the numbers of babies in multiples were not differentiated, these babies were treated in one category as multiples concerning live births.

2) Outline of Japanese ART Data

Almost all medical institutions performing ART are registered with the JSOG. The JSOG administers questionnaire surveys for these medical institutions. The number of medical institutions and response rate (= responding institutions/total institutions) for ART surveillance was shown in Figure 2, which was not high during the early periods. Some of the survey data is presented in annual reports (with no information available in English). All available ART statistics on multiple births were gathered, combined and re-analyzed.

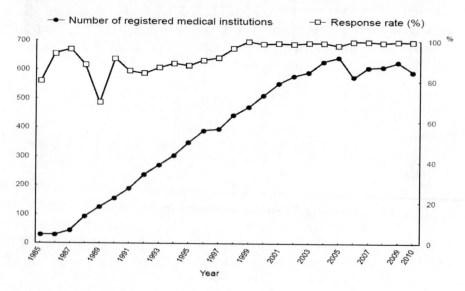

Figure 2. The numbers of medical institutions and response rate for ART surveillance.

The JSOG has gathered ART data from registered institutions since 1985. However, there is incomplete data on the total number of deliveries and live births from 1985-1988, and the author therefore used the 1989-2010 (the latest) data. The data items were not necessarily constant throughout the surveillance period, and data on multiple deliveries/births were not available until 2007. The total number of live deliveries (X) (i.e., number of mothers and live births (Y)), was the only available data throughout 1989-2010. There was no information on the combination of live births and still-births among multiples. The numbers of multiple live births according to subtype (twins, triplets, etc.) were presented only in the 2007-and-after surveys. Among multiple deliveries which contained stillbirths, definitions of "live delivery" and "live births" were as follows: For the multiple pregnancies, the mothers who had at least one live birth neonate were counted as a live delivery. For the multiple births, the births were counted as live only when all neonates in the pair were born alive. For example, if both members of certain twin pairs were alive, then they were counted as two live births (neonates). On the other hand, when one member of certain twin pairs were alive (the other a stillbirth), then they were counted as no live multiple births (neonates), or as one live singleton. No data on maternal age were available. ART was divided into *in vitro* fertilization and embryo transfer (IVF-ET), intracytoplasmic sperm injection (ICSI) using a fresh embryo/egg, and treatment using a frozen embryo, which were the published classification forms in the JSOG annual reports. All these methods were treated as ART in the present study.

2. Statistic Analyses

1) Effect of Maternal Age on Multiple-Birth Rates

First, multiple-birth rates according to maternal age class were analyzed. Next, the number and rates of spontaneous and iatrogenic multiple births were estimated using the following method. The limitation of available data makes it impossible to estimate the relative effect of maternal age and fertility treatment directly.

The spontaneous multiple-birth rate according to maternal age is nearly constant irrespective of the birth year (Bortolus et al., 1999; Bulmer, 1959; Fuster et al., 2008; Hoekstra et al., 2008; Nylander, 1981), at least in Japan (Imaizumi and Inouye, 1979). Using this fact, the number of spontaneous (S) and iatrogenic (I) multiple live births in a certain age class could be estimated as $S=T*s$ and $I=M-S=M-T*s$, respectively (T, total number of live births; M, total number of multiple live births; S, total number of spontaneous multiple live births; I, total number of iatrogenic multiple live births; s, the proportion of spontaneous multiple births of a certain age class [i.e., the age class specific multiple-birth rate]; * means multiplication).

The mean live multiple-birth rates between 1974 and 1976 according to maternal age class were used as the spontaneous live multiple-birth rates, since the occurrence of multiple births by fertility treatment were negligible in this period in Japan. The author used the weighted mean of three years to reduce fluctuation of the data according to year. The number or proportion of naturally conceived multiple births in 1977-2011 was estimated by multiplying the mean age-specific live multiple-birth rates between 1974-1976 by the age-specific total number of births, including both singletons and multiples, from the 1977-2011 data.

By summing up the numbers of all age classes, the total number of spontaneous multiple births can be estimated, and then the spontaneous multiple-birth rates can be calculated. The number of iatrogenic multiple births were estimated by subtracting the spontaneous multiples from the total multiples; the multiple-birth rates can then be calculated. The theoretical limitations of this method are described later in the DISCUSSION section.

2) Estimation of Numbers and Rates of ART and Non-ART Multiples

It was impossible to calculate the number of ART multiple births directly due to insufficient data, as mentioned in the definitions of live births in ART statistics. Since the following estimation contains many assumptions, the arithmetic mean of the minimum and maximum possible values is provided as an estimate value.

The total number of ART multiple live births was estimated by the following method under the assumption that the percentage of triplets/+ in the total ART births was sufficiently small. Only when the total number of mothers with a live delivery (X=a+b+c) and live neonate (Y=a+2b+3c), where all neonates of the pair are born alive in the case of multiple births, is known, where a, b and c denotes the number of mothers of singletons, twins, and triplets, respectively, can the total number of ART multiple births (2b+3c) be approximated as 2(Y-X)=2b+4c. To adjust for the excess of "c" (2b+4c=2b+3c+c), X*t (* means multiplication) was subtracted, where "t" denotes the triplet/+ pregnancy rate in ART pregnancies, assuming that the triplet/+ pregnancy rate is equal to the triplet/+ live births rate. Thus, the minimum estimation formulae of 2(Y-X)-X*t was obtained.

In the present data, X includes mothers who had multiples, even if some were stillbirths. To exclude mothers of live-stillbirth pairs in multiples, the author used the general stillbirth rates of live-stillbirth twin pairs (k), including both spontaneous and iatrogenic stillbirths, from vital statistics. The number of twin mothers with live-stillbirth pairs (X') was thus estimated by multiplying the total number of multiple deliveries (b+c) and live-stillbirth rates in twin pairs (k). The total number of multiple deliveries in the total ART pregnancies was approximated as Y-X (=b+2c). Thus, X' is approximated as (Y-X)k. The approximation formula for the ART live multiples was 2(Y-(X-X'))=2(Y-(X-(Y-X)k))=2(Y-X)(1+k). Finally, the inverse of the number of response rates was multiplied, assuming that the mean number of ART multiples in responding and non-responding institutions is equal. The final approximation formula for the number of ART multiples was then 2(Y-X)(1+k)/(response rate), which gives a maximum estimation value. As the stillbirth rates of twin pairs were included in the vital statistics after 1995, the 1989-1994 values were extrapolated using approximation formula derived from the 1995-1999 values (cubic function, R^2=.999).

The validity of the estimation method mentioned above was determined using 2007, 2008, 2009 and 2010 data on the observed number of live multiple births with ART. As the estimated error was 0.48-1.00% (observed number was 3,914 and estimated number was 3,933; the difference was 0.50% in 2007, observed number was 2,670 and estimated number was 2,697; the difference was 1.00% in 2008, observed number was 2,727 and the estimated number was 2,740; the difference was 0.48% in 2009, observed number was 2,802 and the estimated number was 2,821; the difference was 0.68% in 2010), this estimation method was valid, at least for the most recent years.

Using the estimated number of ART multiples between 1989-1992, and the fact that the first ART baby was born in Japan in 1983, the number of ART multiple births between 1984-1988 was interpolated using an approximation formula derived from the 1983 and 1989-1992 values. The number of ART multiples between 1979-1982 was set as equal to zero. The number of non-ART iatrogenic multiple births was estimated by subtracting the ART multiples from the total iatrogenic multiples.

3) Theoretical Model of the Relationship Between the Single Embryo Transfer Rate and Multiple Pregnancy Rate

(1) Definitions

In the JSOG ART data, pregnancy is defined as the ascertainment of a gestational sac and not merely a positive reaction to a pregnancy test. Ectopic pregnancies were included.

The pregnancy rate after ART was defined as the total number of pregnancies divided by the total number of times of implantation in the present study. The SET pregnancy rate was defined as the proportion of the number of pregnancies after SET divided by the total number of pregnancies after ART. In the present definition, the SET pregnancy rate was not the pregnancy rate by SET. The multiple pregnancy rate was defined as the proportion of the total number of multiple pregnancies after ART divided by the total number of pregnancies after ART. The non-SET, mainly double-embryo transfer (DET), multiple-pregnancy rate was defined as the proportion of the total number of multiple pregnancies after ART divided by the total number of non-SET pregnancies after ART, which was calculated as (total number of multiple pregnancies)/(total number of pregnancies − total number of SET pregnancies). All rates are shown as percentages in the results.

(2) Theoretical Model

Following is a theoretical model of the relationship between the SET pregnancy rate and the multiple pregnancy rate. In a certain year, the total multiple pregnancy rate (M) is the sum of the multiple pregnancy rate after SET (S) and that after non-SET (D), namely, more than one embryo transfer. If the SET pregnancy rate is s ($0 \leq s \leq 1$), then the non-SET pregnancy rate is 1-s. In addition, if the multiple pregnancy rate after SET pregnancies is p ($0 < p$), and that after non-SET pregnancies is q ($0 < q$), the total multiple pregnancy rate is calculated by the following formula:

$$M = S + D = s*p + (1-s)*q = q-(q-p)*s \quad (* \text{ means multiplication})$$

All multiple pregnancies after SET produce monozygotic (MZ) multiples, mainly MZ twins, and those after non-SET mainly produce polyzygotic multiples, that is, double embryo transfers produce dizygotic twins. Remember, however, that MZ twinning can occur even after non-SET, and thus q also contains a portion of MZ twinning after non-SET.

In the present study the relationship between the SET pregnancy rate and the multiple pregnancy rate was treated as the survival curve of the multiple pregnancy rate (Y-axis) against the SET pregnancy rate (X-axis). To examine this analysis, the author assumed that p and q changed according to the improvement of ART prognosis, the proxy variable of which would be the total pregnancy rate per implantation. Even if p and q both change, it is reasonable to assume that q is larger than p, and thus the survival curve would decrease monotonically.

The survival curve of the multiple pregnancy rate against the SET pregnancy rate was hypothesized to be divided into three periods. (1) First period: When the pregnancy rate per implantation is increasing from a relatively lower level to a higher level, the effect of SET on the multiple pregnancy rate would be small, since multiple embryo transfer does not necessarily produce a multiple pregnancy. The MZ twinning rate after SET (p) would decrease and the multiple pregnancy rate after non-SET (q) would increase according to the improvement of ART, and thus q-p increases in an earlier stage. This means that the theoretical survival curve has a convex upward shape in this period. The multiple pregnancy rate decreases gradually. (2) Second period: When the pregnancy rate per implantation is nearly constant at a high level, the effect of SET on multiple pregnancies rapidly becomes large. According to the above theoretical formula, if both p and q are nearly constant or change within a narrow range, the multiple pregnancy rate decreases linearly with the increase of the s. The multiple pregnancy rate after SET is much lower than that after non-SET, and thus q-p is a positive quantity and is nearly equal to q. (3) Third period: The pregnancy rate per implantation becomes constant or possibly decreases while remaining at a relatively high level, since high-risk-fertility couples do not necessarily achieve pregnancy even with improved ART. In this period, the effect of MZ twinning after SET on the total multiple pregnancy rate would not be ignorable. The multiple pregnancy rate after non-SET (q) may decrease, and thus q-p would also decrease, assuming that p is nearly constant. As a result, the decrease of the multiple pregnancy rate became slow, and the survival curve shows a convex downward shape. As mentioned above, the total survival curve of these three periods is expected to be like a reverse sigmoid curve. Remember that this curve depicts the multiple pregnancy rate against the SET rate, not the calendar year, since the SET rate does not increase constantly against the calendar year.

(3) Statistical Methods

The relationship between the SET pregnancy rate and the multiple pregnancy rate was examined by using limited Japanese national data on ART presented by JSOG. Reliable data on the total pregnancy rate per implantation and the multiple pregnancy rate from 1992 to 2010 is available.

The information on the SET was added from 2007 to 2010. The proportion of eSET among total SET, however, was not reported. The mean response rate for ART surveillance between 2007 and 2010 was 99.3%

(2,415/2,431), meaning it is almost all of the data reflecting the current situation of SET and multiple pregnancies in Japan.

First, the author calculated the secular trend between the total pregnancy rate and the multiple pregnancy rate. Then, the author calculated the SET pregnancy rate, multiple pregnancy rate, non-SET pregnancy rate and total pregnancy rate according to the type of ART method employed. Finally, the relationship between the SET pregnancy rate and the multiple pregnancy rate from 2007 to 2010 was plotted, and linear, cubic and exponential approximations were performed. The cubic approximation of four points theoretically produced a perfect fit ($R^2=1$).

Results

1. The Effects of Fertility Treatment and Maternal Age on the Multiple-Birth Rate

1) Outline of the Maternal Age in Japan

In the following results the secular trends of maternal age classes under 20 years and 40 years or more in the Figures were omitted, because the fluctuation of the numbers are too large. Figure 3 and Figure 4 show the maternal age class distribution according to plurality. As to singletons, the decrease in births to mothers aged 25-29 is remarkable. On the other hand, the numbers of singletons born to mothers 30-34 years have been substantially constant in recent years. As to multiple births, those to women 30-34 and 35-39 years are increasing and those to women 20-24 and 25-29 years are decreasing overall.

Figure 5 shows multiple-birth rates according to maternal age classes. Multiple-birth rates were nearly constant until the mid-1980s, with slightly higher births rates in older mothers. The difference in multiple-birth rates by age became wider after the mid-1980s. This tendency was most obvious in the 35-39 age class.

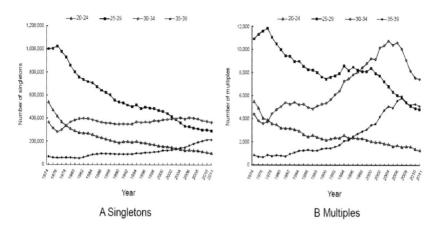

Figure 3. Secular trends of birth numbers according to maternal age class, 1974-2011.

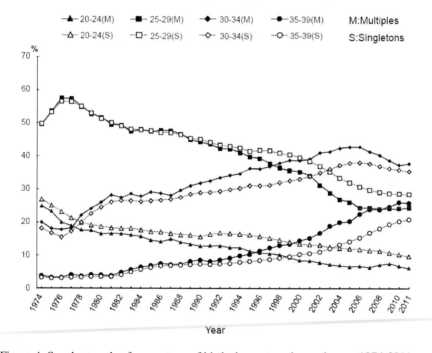

Figure 4. Secular trends of percentage of births by maternal age classes, 1974-2011.

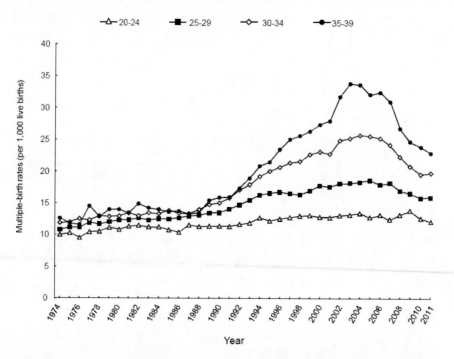

Figure 5. Secular trends of multiple-birth rates according to maternal age, 1974-2011.

Although not shown in Figure, the multiple-birth rates according to maternal age class between 1974-1976 were nearly the same across the three years and tended to increase linearly from age class 20-24 to 30-34 years, supporting the well established fact that spontaneous multiple-birth rates according to maternal age class would be constant. Thus, the author used the weighted mean of three years (i.e., 8.7 in ≤19, 9.9 in 20-24, 11.0 in 25-29, 12.1 in 30-34, 12.0 in 35-39, and 10.2 in ≥40 years per 1,000 live births).

2) Effect of Maternal Age on Spontaneous and Iatrogenic Multiple Births

Figure 6 shows the estimated number of multiple births according to the maternal age class and the method of conception. The number of iatrogenic multiple births (B) were calculated by subtracting the number of spontaneous multiples (A) from the total number of multiples (Figure 3B). The number of spontaneous multiple births drastically decreased for 25-29 year-olds, but remained nearly constant for 30-34 year-olds. The number of iatrogenic multiple births was markedly increased for 30-34 year-olds and 35-39 year-olds, and recently decreased.

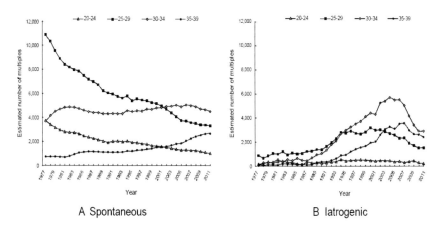

A Spontaneous   B Iatrogenic

Figure 6. Estimated number of multiple births in Japan according to the method of conception and maternal age class, 1977-2011.

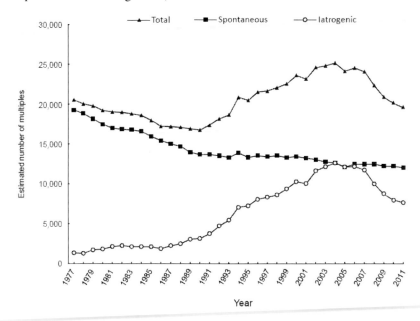

Figure 7. Secular trends in the sum of the age-specific estimated number of spontaneous and iatrogenic multiple births, 1977-2011.

Figure 7 shows the secular trend of the sum of the age-specific estimated number of spontaneous and iatrogenic multiple births. The number of spontaneous multiple births decreased constantly, whereas that of iatrogenic multiple births increased gradually until the mid-1980s and then rapidly increased. The estimated maximum percentage of iatrogenic multiple births among total multiple births was 50.0% in 2004 and 2005, then decreased to 38.9% in 2011.

Regarding the multiple-birth rates, spontaneous multiple-birth rates showed a slight increase from 11.0 (1977) to 11.4 (2011) because the distribution of maternal age shifted higher with years. On the other hand, those of iatrogenic multiple births gradually increased from 0.7 (1977) to 1.3 (1986), rapidly and dramatically increased from 1.3 (1986) to 11.4 (2005), and then decreased to 7.3 (2011). The rapid increase of the multiple-birth rate after the mid-1980s was almost entirely attributed to iatrogenic multiple births.

2. Estimation of the Effect of ART and Non-ART Ovulation Stimulation Fertility Treatments on the Number and Rate of Multiple Live Births

Figure 8 shows secular trends of the multiple pregnancy rate in the total ART pregnancies. The twinning rate gradually decreased to 14% in 2005, then decreased rapidly to 5% in 2010. The triplets/+ rate gradually linearly decreased from 2% in 1997 to almost 0% in 2008.

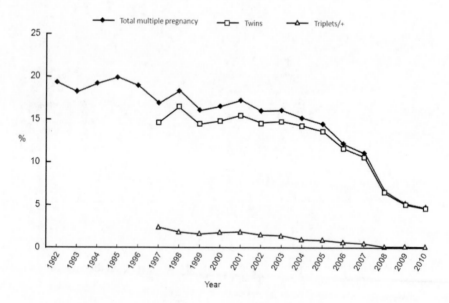

Figure 8. Percentage of multiple pregnancies in ART.

Figure 9 shows the percentage of twin pregnancies in the total ART multiple pregnancies. In recent years, the percentage has tended to increase linearly, reaching 98% between 2008 and 2010.

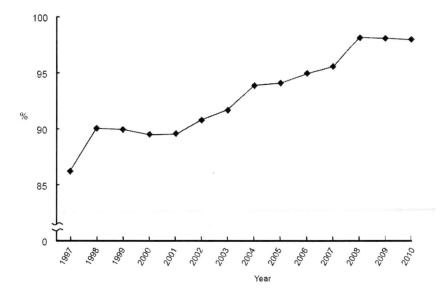

Figure 9. Percentage of twin pregnancies in ART multiple pregnancies.

Figure 10 shows the estimated number and rates of ART and non-ART live multiples with the total iatrogenic and spontaneous multiple births. As mentioned in the METHODS section, the 1984-1988 values for ART were interpolated using the approximation formula (cubic function, R^2=.998).

There was an overall increase in the ART and non-ART iatrogenic multiple births until 2005 and 2007, respectively. ART multiples tended to rapidly and linearly decrease from 2005 to 2008. Nonetheless, this decrease stopped after 2008.

The rate of non-ART multiples increased gradually, peaking in 2007 or 2008, then decreased over the next three years. The number or rate of ART multiples was almost consistently lower than that of non-ART ovulation stimulation multiples. In 2010, the percentages of births by spontaneous conception, ART and non-ART fertility treatments were 60%, 14% and 26%, respectively.

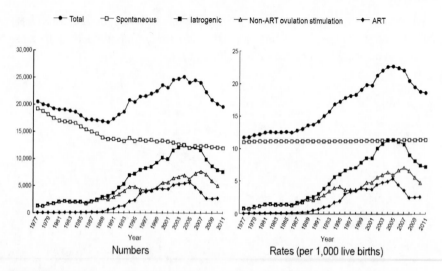

Figure 10. Estimated numbers and rates of multiple births in Japan according to the method of conception.

The percentage of non-ART multiple births in iatrogenic multiples tended to be higher than ART multiples. Almost all of the iatrogenic multiples occurred due to non-ART before 1988. The percentage of ART multiples in iatrogenic multiples was small in 1989 (8%), but gradually increased, peaking at around 50% between 1998-1999. The percentage rapidly decreased beginning in 2005, falling to 27% in 2008, and then again increased to 35% in 2010.

3. Theoretical Model of the Relationship Between the Single Embryo Transfer Rate and Multiple Pregnancy Rate

The secular trend of the total pregnancy rate and multiple pregnancy rate after ART is shown in Figure 11. The total pregnancy rate was nearly constant from 1992 to 1998 (21-23%). It then gradually increased and then tended to become constant around 30%. The multiple pregnancy rate was nearly constant (18-20%) from 1992 to 1996. It then decreased.

The SET pregnancy rate, multiple pregnancy rate and non-SET multiple pregnancy rate are shown with the total pregnancy rate according to the main methods of ART in Table 1.

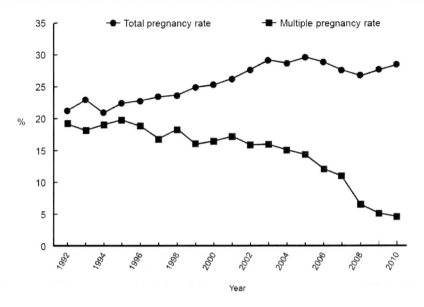

Figure 11. Secular trend of the total pregnancy rate and multiple pregnancy rate, 1992-2010.

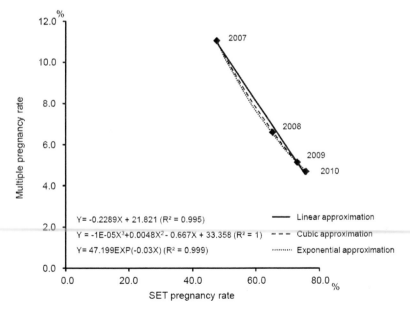

Figure 12. The multiple pregnancy rate plotted against SET pregnancy rate from 2007 to 2010 with linear, cubic and exponential approximations.

Table 1. SET Pregnancy Rate, Multiple Pregnancy Rate, Non-SET Multiple Pregnancy Rate and Total Pregnancy Rate According to the ART Type

		SET pregnancy rate	Multiple pregnancy rate	Non-SET multiple pregnancy rate	Total pregnancy rate per implantation
Fresh	IVF-ET				
	2007	41.3 (3,017/7,313)	12.7 (926/7,313)	21.6 (926/4,296)	26.4 (7,313/27,729)
	2008	60.0 (4,082/6,808)	7.5 (513/6,808)	18.8 (513/2,726)	23.8 (6,808/28,609)
	2009	69.3 (4,725/6,818)	5.8 (397/6,818)	19.0 (397/2,093)	24.3 (6,818/28,075)
	2010	71.7 (4,651/6,484)	5.2 (337/6,484)	18.4 (337/1,833)	23.7 (6,484/27,378)
	ICSI				
	2007	39.3 (2,585/6,577)	11.3 (746/6,577)	18.7 (746/3,992)	22.1 (6,577/29,768)
	2008	55.8 (3,314/5,934)	7.2 (425/5,934)	16.2 (425/2,620)	19.9 (5,934/29,831)
	2009	63.4 (3,921/6,186)	5.7 (354/6,186)	15.6 (354/2,265)	20.2 (6,186/30,604)
	2010	67.6 (4,320/6,393)	4.9 (315/6,393)	15.2 (315/2,073)	20.1 (6,393/31,770)
Frozen					
	2007	55.7 (7,757/13,932)	9.9 (1,376/13,932)	22.3 (1,376/6,175)	32.1 (13,932/43,452)
	2008	71.0 (12,913/18,194)	6.0 (1,086/18,194)	20.6 (1,086/5,281)	32.2 (18,194/56,494)
	2009	76.7 (17,500/22,813)	4.7 (1,079/22,813)	20.3 (1,079/5,313)	32.6 (22,813/69,979)
	2010	78.5 (21,129/26,905)	4.4 (1,195/26,905)	20.7 (1,195/5,776)	33.7 (26,905/79,944)
Total					
	2007	47.5 (13,865/29,165)	11.0 (3,221/29,165)	21.1 (3,221/15,300)	27.6 (29,165/105,849)
	2008	65.3 (21,232/32,511)	6.6 (2,139/32,511)	19.0 (2,139/11,279)	26.8 (32,511/121,395)
	2009	73.0 (27,330/37,437)	5.1 (1,917/37,437)	19.0 (1,917/10,107)	27.7 (37,437/135,093)
	2010	75.7 (31,503/41,637)	4.7 (1,946/41,637)	19.2 (1,946/10,134)	28.4 (41,637/146,377)

SET: single embryo transfer.
ART: assisted reproductive technology.
IVF-ET: *in vitro* fertilization and embryo transfer.
ICSI: intracytoplasmic sperm injection.
For definitions of rates, see the text.

Table 2. Approximation Formula with R^2

Types of ART	Approximation formula Linear approximation	Cubic approximation	Exponential approximation
Fresh			
IVF-ET	$Y = -0.2439X + 22.576$ ($R^2=0.993$)	$Y = -0.0003X^3 + 0.0566X^2 - 3.5738X + 85.678$ ($R^2=1$)	$Y = 41.432\exp(-0.029X)$ ($R^2=0.998$)
Y (X=100)	-1.81	-5.70	2.28
ICSI	$Y = -0.2286X + 20.21$ ($R^2=0.995$)	$Y = -9E\text{-}05X^3 + 0.0164X^2 - 1.2144X + 39.041$ ($R^2=1$)	$Y = 35.943\exp(-0.029X)$ ($R^2=0.998$)
Y (X=100)	-2.65	-11.10	1.98
Subtotal	$Y = -0.2365X + 21.463$ ($R^2=0.992$)	$Y = -0.00002X^3 + 0.0288X^2 - 1.9606X + 54.521$ ($R^2=1$) [a]	$Y = 38.767\exp(-0.029X)$ ($R^2=0.999$)
Y (X=100)	-2.19	-53.54	2.13
Frozen			
Frozen (intra-uterine)	$Y = -0.241X + 23.24$ ($R^2=0.998$)	$Y = 0.0003X^3 - 0.0495X^2 + 2.957X - 45.009$ ($R^2=1$) [a]	$Y = 69.573\exp(-0.035X)$ ($R^2=0.998$)
Y (X=100)	-0.86	55.69	2.10
Subtotal	$Y = -0.2378X + 23.024$ ($R^2=0.997$)	$Y = 0.0002X^3 - 0.0384X^2 + 2.206X - 28.318$ ($R^2=1$)	$Y = 67.063\exp(-0.034X)$ ($R^2=0.998$)
Y (X=100)	-0.76	8.28	2.24
Grand total	$Y = -0.2289X + 21.821$ ($R^2=0.995$)	$Y = -1E\text{-}05X^3 + 0.0048X^2 - 0.667X + 33.358$ ($R^2=1$)	$Y = 47.199\exp(-0.03X)$ ($R^2=0.999$)
Y (X=100)	-1.07	4.66	2.35

ART: assisted reproductive technology.

IVF-ET: *in vitro* fertilization and embryo transfer.

ICSI: intracytoplasmic sperm injection.

X: SET pregnancy rate. Y: Multiple pregnancy rate.

[a] These two approximation formulae was not convex downward with monotonic decrease.

The SET pregnancy rate rapidly increased during 2007-2010, reaching over 75%, while the multiple pregnancy rate decreased to less than 5% (2010), with no dramatic change in the total pregnancy rate. The non-SET multiple pregnancy rate was nearly constant (19-21% in total) irrespective of the ART method. This value was near that of the multiple pregnancy rate from 1992 to 1996. The SET pregnancy rate was higher in cases of frozen embryo transfer compared to IVF-ET and ICSI.

The total multiple pregnancy rate plotted against the SET pregnancy rate is shown in Figure 12. The scatter plot tended to decrease linearly. Thus, the regression line was reasonably linear. With this result, the following approximation was performed.

Linear, cubic and exponential approximation formulae with corresponding R^2s according to the ART methods are shown in Table 2. The multiple pregnancy rate (Y) when the SET pregnancy rate (X) is 100%, which means MZ multiple pregnancy rate after SET, in the approximation formula is also shown. The multiple pregnancy rates all decreased linearly with the increase of the SET pregnancy rate, irrespective of the ART method. All R^2s were more than 0.99. The regression coefficients of linear approximation were around - 0.23 - -0.24, irrespective of the ART method. When the SET rate was equal to 0%, the Y-intercept of the regression line was 20-23%. Exponential approximations also fit very well. When the SET rate was equal to 100%, the multiple pregnancy rate was estimated to be about 2% in total by using exponential approximation formulae, showing the MZ multiple pregnancy rate after SET. The effect of SET on the decrease of multiple pregnancies, which was shown by the coefficient of the exponential curve, was more obvious in frozen embryo transfer compared to IVF-ET or ICSI. These results remain unchanged if all analyses were performed by excluding ectopic pregnancies.

Discussion

1. The Effect of Maternal Age and Fertility Treatment on Multiple Births Rate

The results of the estimated numbers of spontaneous multiple births in Figure 6A, which were estimated by multiplying the mean age-specific multiple-birth rates between 1974-1976 by the age-specific number of births from 1977-2011 data, as a matter of course closely reflect the secular trend of the numbers of singletons according to maternal age class, shown in Figure

3A. This result also suggests that the influence of advanced maternal age on increased spontaneous multiple births is not so large.

Although mothers aged 30-34 have accounted for the largest proportion of multiple births recently, the real number of spontaneous multiple births of this age class is nearly constant (Figure 6A). Therefore, the substantial change of number of multiples in the 30-34 age class could mainly be attributed to iatrogenic multiples (Figure 6B). Although the estimated number of spontaneous multiples born to women aged 35-39 has increased, the decrease of such births to women aged 25-29 is more dramatic (Figure 6A). This secular trend was similar to those of singletons, which showed the gradual increase of births to woman aged 35-39, and a drastic decrease of births to woman aged 25-29 (Figure 3A). Overall, the total number of spontaneous, multiple live births is decreasing (Figure 7).

Most countries have no official data on non-ART ovulation stimulation (Schieve et al., 2009). This is one of the challenges of epidemiologic monitoring systems of iatrogenic births. The present study showed that the secular trends of multiples in Japan could mainly be attributed to iatrogenic, not spontaneous multiples, in older women, especially 30-34 yearolds, as shown in Figure 6B.

The limitation of the present study was that the present data could not directly separate fertility treatment and confounding factors such as maternal age and parity (Bulmer, 1959). Parity is independent factor that affects spontaneous dizygotic twinning (Bulmer, 1959). The dizygotic, but not the monozygotic, twinning rate increases with parity. As to parity, the number of children born to each mother is rapidly decreasing in Japan, because of complicated socioeconomic factors; for example, the later marriage of women and increase in the proportion of working women. Recently, parity is showing a decrease in mothers of multiples in Japan. For example, about 40% of mothers were estimated to have given birth to their multiples in the first delivery in 1979, whereas that percentage was about 45% in 1989, and around 60% between 1999 and 2011. These estimations were made by using the data on the numbers of live birth multiples according to birth order as individual neonates presented in vital statistics. For example, the number of second deliveries were estimated by subtracting the number of second-born multiples from first-born multiples. Therefore, the effect of parity on spontaneous twinning seems to have weakened.

There are other factors that affect multiple-birth rates, particularly the spontaneous dizygotic twinning rate (Basso et al., 2004; Hoekstra et al., 2008, 2010; Reddy et al., 2005). The effect of maternal physique has been reported recently. Taller mothers and mothers with a high body mass index have a greater likelihood of dizygotic twinning. Smoking, contraceptive use, seasonality and folic acid show a less convincing association with multiple births. The influence of these factors has not been analyzed using Japanese data. But the effects of these factors are small compared with maternal age, by measure of the results of other countries (Basso et al., 2004; Hoekstra et al., 2010; Reddy et al., 2005).

2. Estimation of Iatrogenic Multiples and Rates of ART and Non-ART Multiples

The present study also determined the number of ART and non-ART multiples in iatrogenic multiples during the past thirty years in Japan. Even though the author had to use several assumptions to make the present estimation, the estimation was made because the secular trend of non-ART multiples is unknown, in contrast to its importance. If precise data on iatrogenic or ART pregnancies/births were offered annually, there would be no need for this cumbersome estimation. Given the limitation of available data, the estimation method itself is not necessarily to be discussed in detail. However, the small estimated error showed that there were no serious mistakes in the present estimation, at least for the most recent years.

The 1996 JSOG guidelines for ART stated that embryo transfer should be limited to three, while the 2008 guidelines specified single embryo transfer (Gelbaya et al., 2010). The secular trends of ART multiples may reflect these policies. As shown in Figures 8 and 9, ART multiple pregnancies have rapidly decreased in recent years, especially for that of triplets/+. On the other hand, the total numbers of ART live deliveries (X) and births (Y) are still increasing, suggesting that the number of ART singletons have recently increased. As shown in Figure 10, the rapid increase of ART multiple births after the late 1980s slowed between 1994 and 2005, and then reversed, rapidly decreasing after 2005. These trends reflect the ART policy in Japan. This decrease stopped after 2008. The reason was unclear. The rate of non-ART multiples increased gradually, peaking in 2007 or 2008, then decreased over the past two years, suggesting the improvement of the ovulation stimulation method.

Several hospital-based studies with relatively small sample sizes have reported the percentage of multiples with non-ART fertility treatments. According to Pinborg et al. (2003a), 17% (n=566) of non-IVF/ICSI twins received ovulation stimulation in 1997. In a New Zealand study with data for the period 1996-2001, Bolton et al. (2003) estimated that multiple births conceived by ovulation induction constituted 37% (n=201) of the multiples from fertility treatment. Jones (2007) used U.S. vital statistics and CDC (Centers for Disease Control) ART data, and estimated the contribution of 2000-2003 non-ART (ovulation induction and enhancement) fertility treatments in multiple births. The method used in this study was very simple; the natural twin and triplet/+ birth rate of 1980 was constant and applied to the years 2000-2003. The results show that the percentage of non-ART multiples in the total multiple births increased slightly from 31 to 34%, and ART multiples in the total multiple births also increased from 7% to 9% (recalculation by present author using Table 1 and Table 2 in the article, which showed the total and non-ART twin and triplet/+ births, respectively). In a recent study, Schieve et al. (2009) used U.S. vital statistics and CDC's ART data to estimate the contribution of non-ART ovulation stimulation fertility treatments to multiple births in the U.S. The percentage of iatrogenic multiple births due to fertility treatments in 2005 was 40.1% (17.3% for ART, 22.8% for non-ART). These values are about 10% lower than the present results in the same year (50.0% in total, 22.8-24.6% for ART, 25.5-27.2% for non-ART). Although secular trends in the U.S. are unclear, ART multiples still seemed higher in Japan during this period. However, according to Park et al. (2010), the total ART multiple births was 14.7% of the entire multiple births in 2006 in Korea (19.2-20.2% in Japan).

Estimations of the percentage of ART and/or non-ART multiple births vary widely, according to the reports. These cross-sectional results should be interpreted carefully, since secular trends differ between countries due to the influence of ART policies. For example, the multiple birth rate was still increasing in Korea even in 2008, while it declined beginning in 2006 in Japan.

In estimating the influence of fertility treatments, non-ART should be considered. According to Tandberg et al. (2007), the twinning rate increased 50% in Norway during the years 1988-2004, even after excluding pregnancies from ART. These researchers concluded that neither pregnancies from ART nor delayed child bearing could explain the rise in the twinning rate. However, the effect of non-ART fertility treatments, which could be strongly confounded with maternal age, was not considered.

The author demonstrated that in Japan non-ART ovulation induction is currently associated with a higher percentage of multiple births than ART; thus, non-ART treatments are very likely associated with an even higher proportion of multiple gestation pregnancies overall. To date, no accurate population-based tracking system exists for births resulting from a non-ART treatment.

This study has several limitations. First, in estimating ART multiples, the author assumed that the percentage of triplets/+ in total ART births was significantly lower than that of twins. This assumption may not be true in the earlier years of ART data collection, as shown in Figure 9. The percentage of triplets/+ pregnancies in total multiples was more than 10% before 2002, although the percentage of triplets/+ is likely to be lower in deliveries than in pregnancy, since abortion or stillbirths are more likely to occur in triplets/+ than in twins. Second, the author assumed that the general, including both spontaneous and iatrogenic, stillbirth rates of live-stillbirth twin pairs (k) per multiple delivery (number of mother) was equal to that in ART multiple deliveries. Since the general stillbirth rate includes artificial abortion, this value may be higher than that in ART. If this is the case, then estimation by the approximation formula of the present study slightly favors the overestimation of ART multiple births. Third, the correction of the response rate of the ART survey had to have been inaccurate in earlier periods, since the response rates were low between 1989 and 1997. If institutions that did not perform ART did not respond, then the correction the author made for the response rate overestimates ART multiple births. Nevertheless, the present results offer an important overview of the secular trend of ART and non-ART iatrogenic multiples.

Mothers of multiple-birth children are clearly older than mothers of singletons. For example, the percentage of mothers of 35 years or more in multiples is 23%, compared with 16% in singletons in 2005, and 31% and 25% in 2011, respectively (Figure 4). Moreover, the estimated maximum percentage of multiple births that were iatrogenic was 50% in 2004 and 2005. Their advanced age makes the physical, mental and social burden of rearing two babies at once even greater. This situation could increase the risk of maternal problems, for example postpartum depression, difficulties with child rearing, and in the worst case child maltreatment (Bryan et al., 1997; Denton, 2005; Tanimura et al., 1990; Thorpe et al., 1991).

Although the number of iatrogenic multiples has recently decreased due to the decrease of ART multiple births based on the SET policy (Gelbaya et al., 2010), the relative contribution of non-ART multiple births are increasing. Considering the medical and social impact of all types of iatrogenic multiple births (Callahan and Greene, 1998; Hall and Callahan, 2005; Ooki, 2006; Scholz et al., 1999), there is an urgent need for a hospital-based monitoring system for fertility treatments, especially for non-ART and multiple births.

3. *Theoretical Model of Estimating the Number of Non-ART Multiple Births*

The estimation by approximation formulae of the present study is in favor of overestimating spontaneous multiple births (Ooki, 2010b), since the maternal age distribution of all live births, including both singletons and multiples, between 1977-2011 is assumed to be spontaneous, while in fact some are iatrogenic. In other words, the present results underestimate the numbers of iatrogenic multiples. Logically, the author should have excluded iatrogenic infants from this calculation. This was impossible, however, since the main target of estimation was the number of non-ART iatrogenic infants. There is no other conclusive method for estimating the numbers of iatrogenic multiples under the present circumstances with no complete registry of fertility treatment, especially for non-ART and multiples (Ooki, 2010b).

Following is a theoretical estimation method. In a certain maternal age class in a certain birth year, the total number of multiple live births (M) is the sum of spontaneous (S) and iatrogenic (I) multiple births. If the proportion of all live births after fertility treatment is x (0<x<1), the proportion of all spontaneous live births is 1-x. Then, the total number of spontaneous births is T*(1-x), where T is the total number of live births, including both singletons and multiples (* means multiplication).

In the same manner, the total number of iatrogenic births is T*x. If the spontaneous multiple birth rate of a certain age class is s (0<s<1), the number of spontaneous live multiple births of this age class (S) is T*(1-x)*s. If the proportion of live multiple births among all live births after fertility treatment is i (0<i<1), then the number of iatrogenic live multiple births (I) is T*x*i. Therefore, the total number of multiple live births (M) in this age class is calculated using the following formulae.

$$M=S+I=T*(1-x)*s+T*x*i$$

By transposing the terms, the following formula is obtained:

$$D=M/T-s=x*(i-s)$$

In this formula, M/T is the total live multiple birth rate. Therefore, D=M/T-s shows the iatrogenic multiple birth rate.

If i is sufficiently larger than s, and x is relatively small, then x*(i-s) is approximated as x*i. Using this approximation formula, the number or percentage of spontaneous and iatrogenic multiple births could be estimated as follows:

I=T*x*i is approximated to T*(M/T-s)=M-T*s

S=M-I is approximated to M-(M-T*s)=T*s

Schieve et al., (2009) accordingly used these approximation formulae to calculate S. The degree of overestimation of spontaneous multiple births is mathematically T*s-T*(1-x)*s=T*s*x. As x and i are unknown, the appropriateness of estimating the total number or percentage of iatrogenic multiple births cannot be verified. If these approximations are not realized, the estimation becomes incorrect.

4. Theoretical Model of the Relationship Between Single Embryo Transfer Rate and Multiple Pregnancy Rate

1) Theoretical Model

Given the limitation of available data, the estimation method itself need not necessarily be discussed in detail. The present results overall suggested that the theoretical model of a reverse sigmoid curve or similar pattern curve, although most parts were close to a straight line, fit well for the multiple pregnancy rate against the SET pregnancy rate.

The multiple pregnancy rate decreased almost linearly at least when the SET pregnancy rate was between 40% (IVF-ET and ICSI in 2007) and 80% (frozen embryo transfer in 2010), as shown in Table 1 and Table 2. This also meant that multiple pregnancy rates decreased linearly at least from 13% to 4%, correspondingly. According to the linear approximation, the regression coefficient (=p-q, see Statistic Analyses 3.3 in the METHODS section) was constantly near -0.23- -0.24, irrespective of the ART method, suggesting that q-p (the non-SET multiple pregnancy rate minus the SET multiple pregnancy rate) in the theoretical formula was near constant. If the SET multiple pregnancy rate is estimated to be around 2%, as mentioned later, then the non-SET multiple pregnancy rate is around 25-26% (if -0.23≤p-q≤-0.24 and p=0.02 then 0.25≤q≤0.26). This value is slightly lower than the recent total pregnancy rate (27-28%) shown in Table 1, but it is clearly higher than the expected pregnancy rate of two independent embryo transfers, meaning the DET procedure results in many more instances of multiple pregnancy than singleton pregnancy due to one-embryo abortions.

The linear approximation overestimated multiple pregnancy rates in an earlier period. The multiple pregnancy rate from 1992 to 1997 (18-20%) and the estimated non-SET multiple pregnancy rate (19-21%) were nearly consistent, and they were slightly lower than the Y-intercept of linear approximation (20-23%). If this value is reliable as the non-SET multiple pregnancy rate, the effect of SET on the decrease of multiple pregnancy may be gradual.

There have been few studies that analyzed the secular trend of the SET rate and multiple pregnancy rate. Among them, De Sutter et al. (2003) found that eSET increased from 1.5% (1997-1998) to 17.5% (1999-2002) of all transfers. Comparing these two periods, an overall pregnancy rate of 35% and 34% per transfer, respectively, were obtained, while the overall twinning rate dropped from 30% to 21%. De Sutter et al., (2003) concluded that a decline in the twinning rate is feasible without a drop in the overall pregnancy rate. If this tendency is applicable to the present study, the SET rate was very low in 1997, and most multiple pregnancy rates are based on non-SET. This result also supports that the non-SET multiple pregnancy rate in Japan is around 20%.

On the other hand, the linear approximation was underestimated in the later period. The regression line showed that the multiple pregnancy rate reached zero before the SET pregnancy rate became 100%, suggesting a non-linear decrease of the multiple pregnancy rate when the SET pregnancy rate reached a certain degree. Moreover, all cubic or exponential approximation curves were convex in the downward direction, also suggesting recent slowing of the decrease in the multiple pregnancy rate.

2) MZ Multiple Pregnancies After SET

It is well established that MZ twin pregnancy increased after the introduction of ART (Blickstein et al., 1999; Derom et al., 1987; Wenstrom et al., 1993). According to the recent systematic review and meta-analysis by Vitthala et al., (2009), the risk of MZ twinning pregnancy/birth in all ART is 0.9%, and it is 2.25 times higher than in the case of natural conception. Only three studies (Blickstein et al., 1999, 2003; Saito et al., 2000) were reported on the incidence of MZ twinning after SET in this systematic review. In these three studies there existed 38 MZ pregnancies in a total of 1,850 pregnancies, namely, an MZ twinning rate of 2.05%. According to the present exponential approximation (see Table 2), the multiple pregnancy rate after 100% of SET was 2.35%, which was in good accordance with the above results. Recent studies (Knopman et al., 2010; Papanikolaou et al., 2010; Verpoest et al.,

2009) also consistently reported MZ twinning rates of 1.9% - 2.2%, whether SET occurred or not. The modeling estimation of the twin live birth rate of eSET showed 2.5% for 32-year-old women, 2.3% for 36-year-old women and 1.9% for 39-year-old women, respectively (Scotland et al., 2011) .

Recently, MZ twinning after blastocyst transfer was reported to be significantly higher compared with cleavage-stage embryo transfer (Kawachiya et al., 2011; Sharara and Abdo 2010), although some studies did not support this finding (Moayeri et al., 2007; Papanikolaou et al., 2010). A recent systematic review and meta-analysis by Chang et al. (2009) showed that the risk of MZ twinning after blastocyst transfer was significantly higher compared with cleavage-stage embryo transfer (odds ratio 3.04). Thus, MZ twinning after ART was associated with prolonged embryo cultures and should be evaluated considering the stage of the embryo. According to the study of Moayeri et al., (2007), the risk of MZ twinning with a blastocyst culture is significantly lower recently because of the improvement in culture conditions and a larger experience with a blastocyst culture. This supports the present assumption that p (the MZ twinning rate after SET) decreased with the advance of ART. Sunde (2007) reported that an eSET policy was started in 2002 in Norway and that SET is performed more than 90% as often as IVF or ICSI, and the multiple pregnancy rate is well below 10%. These results suggest that it is important to examine secular trends and methods of ART, both likely to be confounded, to estimate the MZ twinning rate after ART.

3) Set Policy

The main target of SET is twin-prone younger women (De Neubourg and Gerris, 2006), a group in whom SET is very effective. Preventing ART twins from the remaining groups of patients who attempt it constitutes another and probably tougher challenge, because the overall target group is a heterogeneous mix of patients in very different clinical situations (De Neubourg and Gerris, 2006). This means that 100% of SET implementation is virtually impossible. In fact, the Japanese guideline states that embryo transfer should be limited to one (single embryo transfer) in principle, but that double embryo transfer is permitted for those women who, for example, are aged 35 or more, and who have failed to become pregnant after ART more than two times successively.

Recently, Scotland et al. (2011) performed an excellent modeling study in which they assessed the costs, consequences and cost-utility of eSET versus DET. According to their results, eSET is likely to be the preferred option for most woman aged ≤36 years, and the decision may best be considered on a case-by-case basis for woman aged 37-39 years. Thus, determining the effectiveness of SET requires the examination of many complicated factors, for example, the clinical setting of patients, total pregnancy rate, cost-effectiveness, including patients' quality of life. This is beyond the purpose of the present research.

The multiple birth rate could not be analyzed in the present study because the data was insufficient. The multiple pregnancy rate is important from a biomedical point of view, while the multiple birth rate after ART is more important from social and public health points of view.

PART 2. BIRTH DEFECTS AFTER ASSISTED REPRODUCTIVE TECHNOLOGY IN JAPAN: COMPARISON BETWEEN MULTIPLES AND SINGLETONS, 2004-2010

Introduction

There are many epidemiologic studies on birth defects. Two important factors of comparison when examining the prevalence of birth defects are method of conception (spontaneous vs. iatrogenic or ART) and plurality (singletons vs. twins or multiple births), and the combination of both factors.

Concerning the comparison of birth defects between spontaneous conception and ART, larger studies have suggested that children born after ART have an increased risk of birth defects compared with children conceived spontaneously (Williams and Sutcliffe, 2009; Williams et al., 2010). Data from meta-analyses consistently suggest that the overall risk of major birth defects in children born after ART is about 30% higher than in children conceived spontaneously (Hansen et al., 2005; Rimm et al., 2004). A nationwide survey in Sweden also showed a slightly increased risk for birth defects after IVF, even adjusting for possible confounding factors, such as year of birth, maternal age, and parity (Källén et al., 2010). However, the first large-scale report of birth defects in 15,405 offspring conceived by ART in China found that infants born after IVF/ICSI have a birth defect frequency comparable to that in the general Chinese population (Yan et al., 2011).

Regarding the effect of ART on birth defects according to plurality, many studies and meta-analyses have shown an increased risk for singletons conceived by ART (Helmerhorst et al., 2004; Jackson et al., 2004; Reefhuis et al., 2009), but there is controversy over whether the risk is increased or not in twins born after ART (Helmerhorst et al., 2004; Pinborg et al., 2004a; Reefhuis et al., 2009; Shebl et al., 2009). One contributing factor is that ART usually produces dizygotic twins, who have a better pre- and perinatal outcome than monozygotic twins (Glinianaia et al., 2008; Hall, 2003; Luke and Keith, 1990). According to Joy et al., (2008), chorionisity accounts for most of the differences between naturally conceived twins and ART twins.

Concerning the comparison of birth defects between twins and singletons, it has been reported that the prevalence of birth defects is higher in multiples than in singletons in total (not stratified by the method of conception), as shown in national studies (Glinianaia et al., 2008; Kato and Fujiki, 1992; Layde et al., 1980; Li et al., 2003; Luke and Keith, 1990; Myrianthopoulos, 1976; Tang et al., 2006; Zhang et al., 2011; Zimoń et al., 1998) and in an international study (Mastroiacovo et al., 1999). Some studies, however, found no association between multiple births and birth defects (Campana and Roubicek, 1996; Chen et al., 2009; Doyle et al., 1991; Ghai and Vidyasagar, 1988; Little and Nevin, 1989; Ramos-Arroyo, 1991; Windham and Bjerkedal, 1984). Thus, the findings are still inconsistent.

Moreover, ART data presents a unique opportunity for twin studies, as most twins after ART are DZ. The first step in genetic epidemiologic analyses is to clarify familial aggregation of targeted traits. To identify familial aggregation, it is important to compare the concordance rate (McGue, 1992) of birth defects in DZ twin pairs (i.e., siblings that develop together in the same womb) (Caputo et al., 2005; Grosen et al., 2011) with the prevalence of birth defects in the general population.

The use of ART is becoming widespread in Japan, but there are very few epidemiologic reports on ART and birth defects. One reason is because the collection of the data on ART and birth defects in Japan is not systematically managed by the government, but by several academic societies and it is very difficult for researchers to access personal information. The largest database on ART is managed by the Japan Society of Obstetrics and Gynecology (JSOG).

The largest birth defects data is managed by the International Clearinghouse for Birth Defects Monitoring Systems (ICBDMS) Japan Center, which is a volunteer hospital-based registry covering about 10% of all births in Japan. However, this database does not have detailed information on ART. Vital statistics (birth records) from the Ministry of Health, Labour and Welfare of Japan also list the number of birth defects in neonatal/infant mortality but with no information on ART. These three possible data sources are managed independently, and record linkage is virtually impossible. With these essential limitations on the data collection, the present study was performed.

With this background the present author performed preliminary analyses of the overall prevalence of birth defects after ART in Japan (Ooki, 2011c). The purpose of the present study was to estimate birth defects after ART according to disease classification, and to calculate the relative risk (RR) and 95% confidence interval (CI) with singletons for reference in order to further examine the effect of ART on multiple births. Moreover, the present study calculated the concordance rate of twin pairs and examined familial aggregation of birth defects by adding updated data to those of previous studies (Ooki, 2012b, 2012c).

Materials and Methods

1. Outline of Japanese Birth Defects Data After ART

From 2004 to 2010 (the latest), the individual list of all ART pregnancies resulting in birth defects was presented every year in the JSOG annual reports on ART, mentioned in Part 1 of this chapter. The presented items are method of treatment (IVF, ICSI, frozen embryo transfer and others (duplicative methods), and do not include simple ovulation stimulation/enhancement), blastocyst transfer (yes, no, unknown), maternal age, perinatal outcome (spontaneous/artificial abortion [<22 weeks], stillbirths [≥22 weeks], and live births) and their gestational week, plurality (singleton, twins, triplets/+, and unknown), sex (male, female, unknown), early neonatal infant death up to day 6 (yes, no, unknown), and name of disease. The response rate for ART surveillance between 2004-2010 was 97.7-99.5%, and the mean response rate throughout the 7 years was 99.0% (4,233/4,274), meaning that almost a complete database reflecting the current situation of ART and birth defects in Japan could be constructed.

The author used this case report data as initial information for the present secondary data analyses. All methods of fertility treatment were treated as ART in the present study because the classification of these methods is not necessarily consistent and mutually exclusive.

The types of defects were reclassified according to the International Classification of Diseases, tenth edition (i.e., ICD-10, 2003 version). Diseases that were classified in the category of ICD-10 code Q00-Q99 (i.e., congenital malformations, deformations and chromosomal abnormalities) were selected and analyzed in the present study. Other congenital diseases that were not classified in Q00-Q99, such as congenital hypothyroidism, were excluded.

In this reclassification, 151 out of 1,788 (8.4%) singletons and 33 out of 334 multiples (9.9%) were excluded, with no significant difference in the exclusion percentage between singletons and multiples. In total, 1,938 abortions, stillbirths or live births with birth defects (number of fetuses or neonates), consisting of 1,637 (84.5%) singletons, 292 (15.1%) twins, and 9 (0.5%) triplets were included. Twins and triplets/+ were treated in one category as multiples in the present study.

The number of stillbirths according to plurality were not reported in the JSOG data. The number of total ART live births, singletons and multiples were available from 2007-2010. The author estimated the number of ART singletons and multiples between 2004-2006 using approximation formulae, mentioned in Part 1 of this chapter.

2. Statistical Analyses of Comparison Between Singletons and Multiples

First, demographic and perinatal outcome data were analyzed. Then, the crude percentage of birth defects after ART per pregnancy (number of mothers), and live births according to the disease classification were calculated according to plurality and their RR with the corresponding 95% CI. For multiple pregnancies, pregnancies with at least one fetus/neonate with birth defects were counted as one pregnancy with birth defects. In other words, each twin pair concordant with respect to any birth defects was regarded as one pregnancy with birth defects.

3. Concordance Rates of Twin Pair

All concordant pairs were listed with their demographic data and neonatal outcome. The pairwise and probandwise concordance rates (McGue, 1992) were then calculated for each major organ system category, each subcategory, and, in some cases, each disease.

The pairwise concordance rate is the probability that both members of a twin pair are affected if at least 1 member of the pair is affected. The probandwise concordance rate is the probability that a twin is affected if his/her co-twin is affected. Only probandwise concordance rates can be directly compared with risk rates reported for other familial pairings and with population prevalence figures. Pairwise concordance rates were calculated as $C/(C+D)$, and probandwise concordance rates as $2 \times C/(2 \times C+D)$, where C denotes the number of affected concordant pairs and D denotes the number of discordant pairs (McGue, 1992).

Recurrence risk ratios (RRRs) (Guo, 1998) were used as indicators of familial aggregation of birth defects and were calculated as the ratio of the risk of disease manifestation (which, given that one's relative is affected, corresponding to the probandwise concordance rate of twin pairs in the present study) to the disease prevalence in the general population.

Moreover, the author estimated the recurrence risk of DZ pairs, which have the same genetic resemblance as sib-pairs. According to Edwards (1960), if a targeted disease is determined by multifactorial inheritance, its frequency in sib-pairs or DZ twin pairs approximates the square root of disease prevalence in the general population. Thus, the present study compared the probandwise concordance rate of any birth defect in twin pairs with the estimated recurrence risk in sib-pairs and DZ pairs.

Results

1. Birth Defects of Singletons and Multiples

Demographic and perinatal outcome data of ART pregnancies with birth defects are summarized according to plurality in Table 3. Blastocyst transfer, maternal age and gestational were significantly different between singletons and multiples. Males were more frequent in both singletons and multiples. Early neonatal death was more frequent in multiples, although unknown/missing values of early neonatal death in singletons were very high (26.0%).

The number, rate (per 10,000 pregnancies), RR and 95% CI of birth defects in different organ systems are shown in Table 4. The rate of birth defects was significantly higher in multiple pregnancy when assessed per 10,000 pregnancies (82.2 for singletons, 139.7 for multiples, RR=1.70, 95% CI 1.50-1.93). The RRs per pregnancy were significant with regard to seven main categories, 16 subcategories, and 4 diseases (i.e., ventricular septal defect, tetralogy of Fallot, patent ductus arteriosus (PDA), and exomphalos. The RRs per pregnancy were the highest for congenital malformations of the nervous system (RR=3.51, 95% CI 2.52-4.87).

Table 3. Demographic and Perinatal Outcome Data of ART Pregnancies with Birth Defects of Known Plurality

		Singletons (N=1,637 mothers)		Multiple births (N=280 mothers with 301 fetuses/neonates)		p
		N	%	N	%	
Birth year	2004	84	71.8 [a]	33	28.2 [a]	
	2005	113	77.4	33	22.6	
	2006	150	75.8	48	24.2	
	2007	222	80.4	54	19.6	
	2008	291	87.7	41	12.3	
	2009	387	89.2	47	10.8	
	2010	390	89.7	45	10.3	<0.001
Method of treatment	IVF	379	23.2	69	24.6	
	ICSI	358	21.9	66	23.6	
	IVF and ICSI	56	3.4	14	5.0	
	Frozen embryo transfer	842	51.4	131	46.8	n.s.
	Unknown/missing values	2	0.1	0	0.0	
Blastocyst transfer	Yes	909	55.5	127	45.4	
	No	722	44.1	150	53.6	<0.01
	Unknown/missing values	6	0.4	3	1.1	
Maternal age	20-24	5	0.3	0	0.0	
	25-29	135	8.2	35	12.5	
	30-34	536	32.7	121	43.2	
	35-39	695	42.5	99	35.4	
	40-	266	16.2	25	8.9	
	Range	23-46		25-43		
	Mean±SD	35.3±4.1		34.0±3.9		<0.001
	Median	36.0		34.0		
Gestational weeks	-11	3	0.2	0	0.0	
	12-21	85	5.2	11	3.9	
	22-27	30	1.8	11	3.9	
	28-36	201	12.3	148	52.9	
	37-41	1092	66.7	102	36.4	
	42-	11	0.7	0	0.0	
	Unknown/missing values	215	13.1	8	2.9	
	Range	10-42		12-41		
	Mean±SD	36.6±5.6		34.5±4.7		<0.001
	Median	38.0		36.0		
Sex (fetuses/neonates)	Male	778	47.5	150	49.8	
	Female	622	38.0	123	40.9	n.s.
	Unknown/missing values	237	14.5	28	9.3	
Perinatal outcome (fetuses/neonates)	Abortion (< 22 weeks) [b]	88	5.4	13	4.3	n.s.
	Stillbirths (22 ≤ weeks) [b]	31	1.9	6	2.0	
	Live births	1344	82.1	277	92.0	
	Unknown/missing values	174	10.6	5	1.7	
Abortion	Spontaneous	4	4.5	0	0.0	
	Artificial	60	68.2	11	84.6	
	Unknown/missing values	24	27.3	2	15.4	
Early neonatal death (neonatal death up to day 6 after birth)	Yes	39	2.9	25	9.0	<0.001
	No	950	70.7	210	75.8	
	Unknown/missing values	355	26.4	42	15.2	

[a] Percentage of singletons and multiples within each year were calculated.

[b] Abortion was defined as occurring under 22 weeks of gestation and stillbirth was defined as occurring at 22 or more weeks of gestation in the original data.

Unknown/missing values were excluded in the statistical tests.

n.s.: not significant.

Table 4. Crude Birth Defect Rates and RR in ART (Rate per 10,000 Pregnancies)

Major classification code and small disease classification (International Classification of Diseases, tenth edition, 2003 version)	Singletons		Multiples		RR	95% CI
	N	Rate	N	Rate		
Q00–Q07 Congenital malformations of the nervous system	136	6.8	48	23.9	**3.51**	**2.52-4.87**
Q00 Anencephaly and similar malformations	46	2.3	10	5.0	**2.16**	**1.09-4.28**
Q01 Encephalocele	5	0.3	4	2.0	**7.95**	**2.14-29.60**
Q03 Congenital hydrocephalus	32	1.6	11	5.5	**3.42**	**1.72-6.78**
Q04 Other congenital malformations of brain	16	0.8	8	4.0	**4.97**	**2.13-11.61**
Q05 Spina bifida	31	1.6	11	5.5	**3.53**	**1.77-7.01**
Q10–Q18 Congenital malformations of eye, ear, face and neck	104	5.2	17	8.5	1.62	0.97-2.71
Q10 Congenital malformations of eyelid, lacrimal apparatus and orbit	4	0.2	3	1.5	**7.45**	**1.67-33.29**
Q17 Other congenital malformations of ear	74	3.7	12	6.0	1.61	0.88-2.97
Q20–Q28 Congenital malformations of the circulatory system	595	29.9	130	64.9	**2.17**	**1.80-2.62**
Q20 Congenital malformations of cardiac chambers and connections	40	2.0	5	2.5	1.24	0.49-3.15
Q21 Congenital malformations of cardiac septa	334	16.8	68	33.9	**2.02**	**1.56-2.62**
Q210 Ventricular septal defect	217	10.9	50	24.9	**2.29**	**1.68-3.11**
Q211 Atrial septal defect	81	4.1	10	5.0	1.23	0.64-2.37
Q213 Tetralogy of Fallot	25	1.3	8	4.0	**3.18**	**1.43-7.05**
Q22 Congenital malformations of pulmonary and tricuspid valves	31	1.6	8	4.0	**2.56**	**1.18-5.58**
Q23 Congenital malformations of aortic and mitral valves	22	1.1	3	1.5	1.35	0.41-4.53
Q24 Other congenital malformations of heart	46	2.3	4	2.0	0.86	0.31-2.40
Q25 Congenital malformations of great arteries	96	4.8	34	17.0	**3.52**	**2.38-5.20**
Q250 Patent ductus arteriosus	54	2.7	25	12.5	**4.60**	**2.86-7.39**
Q26 Congenital malformations of great veins	16	0.8	3	1.5	1.86	0.54-6.39

Table 4. (Continued)

Major classification code and small disease classification (International Classification of Diseases, tenth edition, 2003 version)	Singletons		Multiples		RR	95% CI
	N	Rate	N	Rate		
Q27 Other congenital malformations of peripheral vascular system	9	0.5	5	2.5	**5.52**	**1.85-16.47**
Q30-Q34 Congenital malformations of the respiratory system	28	1.4	5	2.5	1.77	0.69-4.59
Q33 Congenital malformations of lung	17	0.9	4	2.0	2.34	0.79-6.95
Q35-Q37 Cleft lip and cleft palate	117	5.9	22	11.0	**1.87**	**1.19-2.95**
Q35 Cleft palate	31	1.6	4	2.0	1.28	0.45-3.63
Q36 Cleft lip	31	1.6	5	2.5	1.60	0.62-4.12
Q37 Cleft palate with cleft lip	55	2.8	13	6.5	**2.35**	**1.28-4.30**
Q38-Q45 Other congenital malformations of the digestive system	141	7.1	25	12.5	1.76	1.15-2.70
Q39 Congenital malformations of oesophagus	27	1.4	7	3.5	**2.58**	**1.12-5.91**
Q40 Other congenital malformations of upper alimentary tract	8	0.4	2	1.0	2.48	0.53-11.70
Q41 Congenital absence, atresia and stenosis of small intestine	21	1.1	5	2.5	2.37	0.89-6.27
Q42 Congenital absence, atresia and stenosis of large intestine	40	2.0	7	3.5	1.74	0.78-3.88
Q423 Congenital absence, atresia and stenosis of anus without fistula	40	2.0	7	3.5	1.74	0.78-3.88
Q43 Other congenital malformations of intestine	30	1.5	2	1.0	0.66	0.16-2.77
Q44 Congenital malformations of gallbladder, bile ducts and liver	10	0.5	2	1.0	1.99	0.44-9.07
Q50-Q56 Congenital malformations of genital organs	63	3.2	13	6.5	**2.05**	**1.13-3.72**
Q53 Undescended testicle	29	1.5	3	1.5	1.03	0.31-3.37
Q54 Hypospadias	28	1.4	9	4.5	**3.19**	**1.51-6.77**

Major classification code and small disease classification (International Classification of Diseases, tenth edition, 2003 version)	Singletons		Multiples		RR	95% CI
	N	Rate	N	Rate		
Q60-Q64 Congenital malformations of the urinary system	84	4.2	8	4.0	0.95	0.46-1.95
Q61 Cystic kidney disease	17	0.9	2	1.0	1.17	0.27-5.06
Q64 Other congenital malformations of urinary system	10	0.5	2	1.0	1.99	0.44-9.07
Q65-Q79 Congenital malformations and deformations of the musculoskeletal system	293	14.7	44	22.0	**1.49**	**1.09-2.05**
Q66 Congenital deformities of feet	33	1.7	4	2.0	1.20	0.43-3.40
Q668 Other congenital deformities of feet	28	1.4	4	2.0	1.42	0.50-4.05
Q69 Polydactyly	70	3.5	11	5.5	1.56	0.83-2.95
Q70 Syndactyly	32	1.6	6	3.0	1.86	0.78-4.46
Q71 Reduction defects of upper limb	9	0.5	2	1.0	2.21	0.48-10.22
Q73 Reduction defects of unspecified limb	3	0.2	2	1.0	**6.62**	**1.11-39.64**
Q75 Other congenital malformations of skull and face bones	13	0.7	2	1.0	1.53	0.35-6.77
Q79 Congenital malformations of the musculoskeletal system, not elsewhere classified	56	2.8	12	6.0	**2.13**	**1.14-3.97**
Q790 Congenital diaphragmatic hernia	24	1.2	4	2.0	1.66	0.58-4.77
Q792 Exomphalos	15	0.8	5	2.5	**3.31**	**1.20-9.11**
Q80-Q89 Other congenital malformations	73	3.7	15	7.5	**2.04**	**1.17-3.56**
Q82 Other congenital malformations of skin	28	1.4	2	1.0	0.71	0.17-2.98
Q87 Other specified congenital malformation syndromes affecting multiple systems	15	0.8	8	4.0	**5.30**	**2.25-12.50**
Q89 Other congenital malformations, not elsewhere classified	28	1.4	4	2.0	1.42	0.50-4.05
Q897 Multiple congenital malformations, not elsewhere classified	10	0.5	2	1.0	1.99	0.44-9.07

Table 4. (Continued)

Major classification code and small disease classification (International Classification of Diseases, tenth edition, 2003 version)	Singletons		Multiples			
	N	Rate	N	Rate	RR	95% CI
Q90-Q99 Chromosomal abnormalities, not elsewhere classified	347	17.4	37	18.5	1.06	0.76-1.49
Q90 Down's syndrome	204	10.2	23	11.5	1.12	0.73-1.72
Q91 Edwards' syndrome and Patau's syndrome	91	4.6	13	6.5	1.42	0.79-2.54
Q913 Edwards' syndrome, unspecified	74	3.7	10	5.0	1.34	0.69-2.60
Q917 Patau's syndrome, unspecified	17	0.9	3	1.5	1.75	0.51-5.98
Any birth defects	1637	82.2	280	139.7	**1.70**	**1.50-1.93**
Excluding patent ductus arteriosus	1583	79.5	255	127.2	**1.60**	**1.40-1.83**

Singleton pregnancies=199,142, Multiple pregnancies=20,043 with 40,988 fetuses/neonates.
RR: relative risk, 95% CI: 95% confidence interval.
Birth defects with at least two cases for both singletons and multiples are shown.
Significant RRs are shown in bold.

The number, rate (per 10,000 live births), RR and 95% CI of birth defects in different organ systems is shown in Table 5. The rate of birth defects was not significantly higher in multiple pregnancies when assessed per 10,000 live births (107.0 for singletons, 98.4 for multiples, RR=0.92, 95% CI 0.81-1.05). RRs were significant regarding congenital malformations of the nervous system (RR=3.29, 95% CI 2.21-4.90). RRs were also significant regarding four subcategories and PDA.

The RRs of any birth defects per pregnancy and of any birth defects per live births both decreased when PDA was excluded.

The crude early neonatal mortality with birth defects in ART and the general population (vital statistics) was calculated, not stratified by plurality due to insufficient information. The early neonatal mortality in ART and non-ART general populations was 4.16 (=64/153,791) and 3.74 (=2,777/7,434,447) per 10,000 live births respectively, and was not statistically significant (RR=1.11, 95% CI 0.87-142).

2. Concordance of Birth Defects in Twins

From among 292 twins with any birth defect, a total of 278 twin pairs were identified: 14 concordant and 264 discordant pairs. Thus, 1.5% (278/19,164) of twin pairs (pregnancies) had at least 1 affected member.

The calculated concordance rates and RRRs are also shown in Table 6. Regarding classification by major organ system, relatively high probandwise concordance rates were observed for congenital malformations of the eye, ear, face, and neck (11.1%); chromosomal abnormalities not elsewhere classified (10.3%); congenital malformations of the circulatory system (9.3%); cleft lip and cleft palate (8.7%); and congenital malformations of the nervous system (8.3%).

Among disease classifications with more than 10 total concordant/ discordant twin pairs, RRRs were relatively high for congenital malformations of the eye, ear, face, and neck (RRR=218, 95% CI 58-815), specifically other congenital malformations of the ear (RRR=425, 95% CI 117-1547); congenital malformations of the great arteries (RRR=203, 95% CI 79-519), specifically those of the patent ductus arteriosus (RRR=445, 95% CI 176-1130); and cleft lip and cleft palate (RRR=149, 95% CI 39-564), specifically a cleft palate with cleft lip (RRR=499, 95% CI 135-1840).

Table 5. Crude Birth Defect Rates and RR in ART (Rate per 10,000 Live Births)

Major classification code and small disease classification (International Classification of Diseases, tenth edition, 2003 version)	Singletons		Multiples			
	N	Rate	N	Rate	RR	95% CI
Q00–Q07 Congenital malformations of the nervous system	57	4.5	42	14.9	**3.29**	**2.21-4.90**
Q03 Congenital hydrocephalus	21	1.7	8	2.8	1.70	0.75-3.84
Q04 Other congenital malformations of brain	9	0.7	10	3.6	**4.96**	**2.01-12.20**
Q05 Spina bifida	24	1.9	11	3.9	**2.04**	**1.00-4.17**
Q10–Q18 Congenital malformations of eye, ear, face and neck	101	8.0	15	5.3	0.66	0.39-1.14
Q10 Congenital malformations of eyelid, lacrimal apparatus and orbit	3	0.2	3	1.1	4.46	0.90-22.10
Q17 Other congenital malformations of ear	72	5.7	10	3.6	0.62	0.32-1.20
Q20–Q28 Congenital malformations of the circulatory system	581	46.2	136	48.3	1.04	0.87-1.26
Q20 Congenital malformations of cardiac chambers and connections	40	3.2	5	1.8	0.56	0.22-1.41
Q21 Congenital malformations of cardiac septa	331	26.3	72	25.6	0.97	0.75-1.25
Q210 Ventricular septal defect	215	17.1	54	19.2	1.12	0.83-1.51
Q211 Atrial septal defect	81	6.4	10	3.6	0.55	0.29-1.06
Q213 Tetralogy of Fallot	24	1.9	8	2.8	1.49	0.67-3.31
Q22 Congenital malformations of pulmonary and tricuspid valves	29	2.3	8	2.8	1.23	0.56-2.69
Q23 Congenital malformations of aortic and mitral valves	20	1.6	3	1.1	0.67	0.20-2.25
Q24 Other congenital malformations of heart	40	3.2	4	1.4	0.45	0.16-1.25
Q25 Congenital malformations of great arteries	96	7.6	36	12.8	**1.67**	**1.14-2.45**
Q250 Patent ductus arteriosus	54	4.3	27	9.6	**2.23**	**1.41-3.54**
Q26 Congenital malformations of great veins	16	1.3	3	1.1	0.84	0.24-2.87

Major classification code and small disease classification (International Classification of Diseases, tenth edition, 2003 version)	Singletons		Multiples			95% CI
	N	Rate	N	Rate	RR	
Q27 Other congenital malformations of peripheral vascular system	8	0.6	5	1.8	2.79	0.91-8.52
Q30-Q34 Congenital malformations of the respiratory system	17	1.4	5	1.8	1.31	0.48-3.56
Q33 Congenital malformations of lung	15	1.2	4	1.4	1.19	0.40-3.58
Q35-Q37 Cleft lip and cleft palate	113	9.0	23	8.2	0.91	0.58-1.42
Q35 Cleft palate	31	2.5	4	1.4	0.58	0.20-1.63
Q36 Cleft lip	31	2.5	5	1.8	0.72	0.28-1.85
Q37 Cleft palate with cleft lip	51	4.1	14	5.0	1.22	0.68-2.21
Q38-Q45 Other congenital malformations of the digestive system	139	11.1	26	9.2	0.83	0.55-1.27
Q39 Congenital malformations of oesophagus	25	2.0	7	2.5	1.25	0.54-2.88
Q40 Other congenital malformations of upper alimentary tract	8	0.6	2	0.7	1.12	0.24-5.25
Q41 Congenital absence, atresia and stenosis of small intestine	21	1.7	5	1.8	1.06	0.40-2.82
Q42 Congenital absence, atresia and stenosis of large intestine	40	3.2	8	2.8	0.89	0.42-1.91
Q423 Congenital absence, atresia and stenosis of anus without fistula	40	3.2	8	2.8	0.89	0.42-1.91
Q43 Other congenital malformations of intestine	30	2.4	2	0.7	0.30	0.07-1.24
Q44 Congenital malformations of gallbladder, bile ducts and liver	10	0.8	2	0.7	0.89	0.20-4.07
Q50-Q56 Congenital malformations of genital organs	63	5.0	13	4.6	0.92	0.51-1.67
Q53 Undescended testicle	29	2.3	3	1.1	0.46	0.14-1.52
Q54 Hypospadias	28	2.2	9	3.2	1.43	0.68-3.04
Q60-Q64 Congenital malformations of the urinary system	71	5.7	8	2.8	0.50	0.24-1.04
Q61 Cystic kidney disease	13	1.0	2	0.7	0.69	0.16-3.04
Q64 Other congenital malformations of urinary system	7	0.6	2	0.7	1.27	0.27-6.14

Table 5. (Continued)

Major classification code and small disease classification (International Classification of Diseases, tenth edition, 2003 version)	Singletons		Multiples			
	N	Rate	N	Rate	RR	95% CI
Q65–Q79 Congenital malformations and deformations of the musculoskeletal system	245	19.5	41	14.6	0.75	0.54-1.04
Q66 Congenital deformities of feet	33	2.6	4	1.4	0.54	0.19-1.53
Q668 Other congenital deformities of feet	28	2.2	4	1.4	0.64	0.22-1.82
Q69 Polydactyly	68	5.4	11	3.9	0.72	0.38-1.36
Q70 Syndactyly	32	2.5	6	2.1	0.84	0.35-2.00
Q71 Reduction defects of upper limb	7	0.6	2	0.7	1.27	0.27-6.14
Q75 Other congenital malformations of skull and face bones	4	0.3	2	0.7	2.23	0.41-12.18
Q79 Congenital malformations of the musculoskeletal system, not elsewhere classified	32	2.5	10	3.6	1.39	0.69-2.84
Q790 Congenital diaphragmatic hernia	16	1.3	4	1.4	1.12	0.37-3.34
Q792 Exomphalos	8	0.6	4	1.4	2.23	0.67-7.41
Q80–Q89 Other congenital malformations	63	5.0	14	5.0	0.99	0.56-1.77
Q82 Other congenital malformations of skin	28	2.2	2	0.7	0.32	0.08-1.34
Q87 Other specified congenital malformation syndromes affecting multiple systems	14	1.1	8	2.8	**2.55**	**1.07-6.08**
Q89 Other congenital malformations, not elsewhere classified	19	1.5	3	1.1	0.70	0.21-2.38
Q897 Multiple congenital malformations, not elsewhere classified	4	0.3	2	0.7	2.23	0.41-12.18
Q90–Q99 Chromosomal abnormalities, not elsewhere classified	198	15.8	31	11.0	0.70	0.48-1.02
Q90 Down's syndrome	141	11.2	20	7.1	0.63	0.40-1.01
Q91 Edwards' syndrome and Patau's syndrome	24	1.9	10	3.6	1.86	0.89-3.89
Q913 Edwards' syndrome, unspecified	26	2.1	8	2.8	1.37	0.62-3.03

Major classification code and small disease classification (International Classification of Diseases, tenth edition, 2003 version)	Singletons		Multiples			
	N	Rate	N	Rate	RR	95% CI
Q917 Patau's syndrome, unspecified	8	0.6	2	0.7	1.12	0.24-5.25
Any birth defects	1344	107.0	277	98.4	0.92	0.81-1.05
Excluding patent ductus arteriosus	1290	102.7	250	88.8	**0.86**	**0.76-0.99**

Singleton live births=125,629; Multiple live births=28,162.

RR: relative risk, 95% CI: 95% confidence interval.

Birth defects with at least two cases for both singletons and multiples are shown.

Significant RRs are shown in bold.

Table 6. Concordance Rates in Twin Pairs and Recurrence Risk Ratios Concerning Birth Defects

Major classification code and small disease classification (International Classification of Diseases, tenth edition, 2003 version)	Twin pairs [a]				Total		RRR (=A/B) (95% CI)
	C (N)	D (N)	Probandwise (A)	Pairwise	N	Prevalence (%) [b] (B)	
Q00–Q07 Congenital malformations of the nervous system	2	44	8.3	4.3	182	0.077	109 (42–281)
Q03 Congenital hydrocephalus	0	11	0.0	0.0	43	0.018	
Q05 Spina bifida	0	11	0.0	0.0	42	0.018	
Q10–Q18 Congenital malformations of eye, ear, face and neck	1	16	11.1	5.9	121	0.051	218 (58–815)
Q17 Other congenital malformations of ear	1	11	15.4	8.3	86	0.037	425 (117–1547)
Q20–Q28 Congenital malformations of the circulatory system	6	117	9.3	4.9	718	0.305	31 (18–53)
Excluding patent ductus arteriosus	4	94	7.8	4.1	639	0.271	29 (15–57)
Q21 Congenital malformations of cardiac septa	2	62	6.1	3.1	398	0.168	36 (14–94)
Q210 Ventricular septal defect	2	45	8.2	4.3	264	0.112	73 (28–189)
Q25 Congenital malformations of great arteries	2	32	11.1	5.9	130	0.056	203 (79–519)
Q250 Patent ductus arteriosus	2	23	14.8	8.0	79	0.034	445 (176–1130)
Q30–Q34 Congenital malformations of the respiratory system	0	5	0.0	0.0	33	0.014	
Q35–Q37 Cleft lip and cleft palate	1	21	8.7	4.5	139	0.059	149 (39–564)
Q37 Cleft palate with cleft lip	1	12	14.3	7.7	68	0.029	499 (135–1840)
Q38–Q45 Other congenital malformations of the digestive system	1	24	7.7	4.0	166	0.070	110 (29–420)
Q50–Q56 Congenital malformations of genital organs	0	13	0.0	0.0	76	0.032	
Q60–Q64 Congenital malformations of the urinary system	0	8	0.0	0.0	92	0.039	

Major classification code and small disease classification (International Classification of Diseases, tenth edition, 2003 version)	Twin pairs [a]				Total		RRR (=A/B) (95% CI)
	C (N)	D (N)	Probandwise (A)	Pairwise	N	Prevalence [b] (%) (B)	
Congenital malformations and							
Q65-Q79 deformations of the musculoskeletal system	1	43	4.4	2.3	337	0.142	31 (8-122)
Q69 Polydactyly	0	11	0.0	0.0	81	0.034	
Q79 Congenital malformations of the musculoskeletal system, not elsewhere classified	0	12	0.0	0.0	68	0.029	
Q80-Q89 Other congenital malformations	0	14	0.0	0.0	87	0.037	
Q90-Q99 Chromosomal abnormalities, not elsewhere classified	2	35	10.3	5.4	384	0.163	63 (25-161)
Q90 Down's syndrome	2	21	16.0	8.7	227	0.096	167 (68-415)
Q91 Edwards' syndrome and Patau's syndrome	0	13	0.0	0.0	104	0.044	
Q913 Edwards' syndrome, unspecified	0	10	0.0	0.0	84	0.035	
Any birth defects	14	264	9.6	5.0	1915	0.812	12 (8-17)
Excluding patent ductus arteriosus	12	241	9.1	4.7	1836	0.778	12 (8-17)

Singleton pregnancies=199,142; Twin pregnancies=19,164; Total fetuses/neonates=237,470.

C: Concordant twin pair, D: Discordant twin pair, CI: Confidence Interval, RRR: recurrence risk ratio.

RRRs were estimated when the concordance rate was not equal to be zero.

[a] The disease classifications with more than 10 concordant/discordant total twin pairs are shown.

[b] Total prevalence was calculated per fetuses/neonates.

[c] Concordance rates and RRR was not shown because of small affected subjects.

Table 7. List of Concordant Pairs

ID	Classification	Maternal age	Gestational weeks	Code	Disease	Sex	Birth status	Early neonatal death	Code	Disease	Sex	Birth status	Early neonatal death	Sex combination
1	Concordance as disease	38	35	Q21 (Q210)	Ventricular septal defect	M	LB	N	Q21 (Q210)	Ventricular septal defect	F	LB	N	OS
									Q21 (Q211)	Atrial septal defect				
									Q25 (Q250)	Patent ductus arteriosus				
2	Concordance as disease	37	26	Q25 (Q250)	Patent ductus arteriosus	M	LB	N	Q25 (Q250)	Patent ductus arteriosus	M	LB	N	MM
3	Concordance as disease	31	27	Q25 (Q250)	Patent ductus arteriosus	M	LB	U	Q25 (Q250)	Patent ductus arteriosus	F	LB	U	OS
									Q32	Congenital malformations of trachea and bronchus				
4	Concordance as disease	35	38	Q22	Congenital malformations of pulmonary and tricuspid valves	F	LB	N	Q42 (Q423)	Congenital absence, atresia and stenosis of anus without fistula	M	LB	N	OS
				Q42 (Q423)	Congenital absence, atresia and stenosis of anus without fistula									
5	Concordance	32	37	Q04	Other congenital	M	LB	N	Q04	Other congenital	M	LB	N	MM

ID	Classification	Maternal age	Gestational weeks	Code	Disease	Sex	Birth status	Early neonatal death	Code	Disease	Sex	Birth status	Early neonatal death	Sex combination
	as subcategory				malformations of brain (lissencephaly)					malformations of brain (lissencephaly)				
6	Concordance as subcategory	32	37	Q04	Other congenital malformations of brain (lissencephaly)	M	LB	N	Q04	Other congenital malformations of brain (lissencephaly)	M	LB	N	MM
7	Concordance as subcategory	30	17	Q17	Other congenital malformations of ear	M	SB	-	Q17	Other congenital malformations of ear	M	SB	-	MM
8	Concordance as subcategory	35	36	Q37	Cleft palate with cleft lip	M	LB	U	Q37	Cleft palate with cleft lip	M	LB	U	MM
9	Concordance as subcategory	31	21	Q73	Reduction defects of unspecified limb (brachymelia)	M	SB	-	Q73	Reduction defects of unspecified limb (brachymelia)	F	SB	-	OS
10	Concordance as major category	40	38	Q20	Congenital malformations of cardiac chambers and connections	F	LB	U	Q21 (Q210)	Ventricular septal defect	F	LB	U	FF

Table 7. (Continued)

ID	Classification	Maternal age	Gestational weeks	Code	Disease	Sex	Birth status	Early neonatal death	Code	Disease	Sex	Birth status	Early neonatal death	Sex combination
11	Concordance as major category	29	33	Q25 (Q250)	Patent ductus arteriosus	M	LB	N	Q20	Congenital malformations of cardiac chambers and connections	M	LB	N	MM
									Q21 (Q210)	Ventricular septal defect				
									Q22	Congenital malformations of pulmonary and tricuspid valves				
									Q27	Other congenital malformations of peripheral vascular system				
12	Concordance as subcategory	34	31	Q90	Trisomy 21 syndrome	M	LB	N	Q90	Trisomy 21 syndrome	M	LB	N	MM
13	Concordance as disease	35	37	Q21(Q210)	Ventricular septal defect	F	LB	N	Q21(Q210)	Ventricular septal defect	F	LB	N	FF
14	Concordance as subcategory	40	36	Q90	Trisomy 21 syndrome	F	LB	N	Q90	Trisomy 21 syndrome	M	LB	U	OS

Listed order of pairs does not mean birth order in twins (first- and second-born).

M: male, F: female; OS: opposite-sexed, LB: live birth, SB: stillbirth; N: no, U: unknown.

Regarding classification code, see also Table

The probandwise concordance rate of any birth defect was 9.6%, which was similar to the estimated recurrence risk among sib-pairs and DZ pairs, namely, 9.0% (the square root of 0.812).

Demographic and perinatal outcome data for all concordant pairs are presented in Table 7. They comprise 7 male–male, 2 female–female, and 5 opposite-sex pairs. Two of the 14 pairs were stillbirth–stillbirth. The records for 8 of the 12 live-birth pairs showed no early neonatal infant death, although the outcome of the other 4 pairs is unknown.

Discussion

1. Comparison Between Multiples and Singletons

1) The Prevalence of Any Birth Defects

The present study for the first time showed the nationwide prevalence of birth defects after ART according to plurality in Japan. However, a direct comparison between the present ART data and birth defects data, and vital statistics (early neonatal mortality rate) may be impossible, because the diagnostic or inclusion criteria for birth defects are not necessarily the same across the dataset. According to Mayor (2010), the risk of a congenital malformation in children born after ART is higher than previously thought, and is a public health issue.

In Japan, the percentage of birth defects per births was reported to be 1.77-2.31% from 2004-2010 according to the report of the ICBDMS Japan Center (http://www.icbdsrj.jp/ data.html, in Japanese, accessed September 2012). The percentage of birth defects per pregnancies and live births increased steadily with year, from 2004 to 2010, for both singletons and multiples in the present study. This tendency was also observed regarding ICBDMS Japan Center reports. Although the definitive reason for this is unclear, one possible reason is that the precision of diagnosis improved. The value presented by the ICBDMS Japan Center is consistently higher than that of ART in the present study. However, direct comparison is impossible, because present rate shown in Table 5 was for live births. Moreover, the method of data collection and diagnosis may be different. Fujii et al. (2010) reported in the recent study that the percentage of birth defects rate in singleton births is 2.3% in IVF and 2.0% in a spontaneous singletons control, using the 2006 JSOG database. According to Fuji et al. (2010), this data is not nationwide, which represents a large proportion of referral hospital data, with a large proportion of the high-risk pregnancy population.

The present percentage of birth defects after ART is lower overall compared with other studies seen in many reviews (Källén et al., 2010; Rimm et al., 2004; Shebl et al., 2009). Nevertheless, the main objective of this study was to evaluate the birth defect rate in multiple births compared to singletons within Japan, and not to compare the birth defect rates across countries. Therefore, the comparison of birth defects in multiple births and singletons may be biased only if there is differential reporting according to plurality, which is not likely to occur (Mastroiacovo et al., 1999).

The percentage of birth defects is clearly higher in multiple pregnancies than in singleton pregnancies with RR around 2 (Table 4), whereas the percentage of birth defects after ART in live ART births is equal in the two groups (Table 5). This seemed reasonable given the fact that birth defects per pregnancy were counted based on the number of pregnant woman, not on the number of fetuses/neonates. The possibility of having at least one fetus/neonate with birth defects, which is counted as one pregnancy with birth defects, is higher in a multiple pregnancy. These results should be examined while considering the number of children in one family. If a certain family has two children after ART, the risk for birth defects is nearly the same, from the family's point of view, whether they are two singletons or one pair of twins.

There exists no direct data indicating the mean number of ART children per family in Japan. According to the vital statistics in Japan, the mean number of children under 6 years old in one family, not stratified by the method of conception, was ca. 1.3-1.4 between 2004 and 2010. If the number of children in one family is the same whether the children are born after ART or spontaneously, than it is suggested that the risk of having birth defects in at least one baby in one family after ART may become higher in families with multiples with at least two children than in families with singletons.

The rate of birth defects per live birth is important for estimating the risk of birth defects of multiple birth babies or for analyzing the etiology of birth defects themselves, while knowing the proportion of birth defects per pregnancy is important for counseling couples who are thinking of undertaking ART. For example, if a couple becomes pregnant with twins, they hope to give birth to two healthy babies, not to at least one healthy baby. Therefore, the risk of birth defects after ART in multiples should be considered in not only the standpoint of births (babies), but maternity or family, as far as the social impact of ART is concerned.

The higher percentage of abortion and/or stillbirth in singletons was observed, as shown in Table 3. The results of the logistic regression analysis for the neonatal outcome of birth defects (whether stillbirths or live births) coincided with this result (data not shown), although the reasons were unclear.

According to Bonduelle et al. (2002), major birth defects after ICSI were found in 3.07% (46/1,499) of the singleton children and in 3.73% (50/1,341) of the children from multiple pregnancies. Major birth defects were found after IVF in 3.15% (49/1,556) of the singleton children and in 4.50% (63/1,399) of the children from multiple pregnancies. The rates of birth defects in multiples were significantly higher than in singletons in ICSI as well as in IVF (p<.05).

Pinborg et al. (2004b) compared twins and singletons after ART (IVF/ICSI) using a Danish national birth cohort and their record linkage. They reported that the rate of major birth defects was not statistically significant between twins and singletons, whereas the total malformation rate (major and minor) was higher in twins than in singletons (p=.001). Other items, such as the risk for stillbirths, preterm delivery, low birthweight, use of cesarean sections and admittance to a neonatal intensive care unit were all higher in twins than in singletons, and the researchers concluded that the neonatal outcome in IVF/ICSI twins is considerably poorer than in singletons.

Birth defects have been the most serious cause of early neonatal mortality, neonatal mortality (within 28 days after birth) and infant mortality in Japan. The early neonatal mortality rate from 2004-2010 attributed to birth defects was consistently around 40%. Given the consistent increase of live births after ART, the impact of ART-related deaths due to birth defects is a public health concern.

As shown in Table 3, follow-up of neonates after ART is insufficient, with almost 26% unknown/missing values for early neonatal mortality. The present values are the minimum numbers, since more early neonatal deaths with birth defects definitely occur in a complete dataset without unknown/missing values. Although the early neonatal mortality rate was not higher in ART than in the general population (RR=1.11, 95% CI 0.87-1.42), precise information concerning definite follow-ups after ART is essential.

2) Each Disease

It is possible that each disease is related to methods of conception (IVF or ICSI), plurality (singletons or multiples), or other factors. For example, some birth defects in the urogenital system of boys are reported to be higher in ICSI than in IVF (Bonduelle et al., 2005; Källén et al., 2005). Patent ductus arteriosus is strongly associated with preterm birth, and may be higher in twins than in singletons (Ericson and Källén, 2001; Pinborg et al., 2004b).

Few studies compared birth defects between singletons and multiples after ART. Of them, Pinborg et al. (2004b) compared neonatal outcomes, including birth defects, between twins and singletons after ART using a Danish national cohort, and concluded that the neonatal outcome in IVF/ICSI twins is considerably poorer than in singletons. For birth defects, the rate of major malformation was not significantly different between twins and multiples, whereas the total malformation rate (major plus minor) was higher in twins than in singletons.

The most common birth defects of major classification were congenital malformations of the circulatory system. This result was in accordance with previous Japanese studies of birth defects in general (Kato and Fujiki, 1992) or other studies (Glinianaia et al., 2008; Mastroiacovo et al., 1999; Pinborg et al., 2004b).

The percentage of some birth defects according to organ system, especially malformations of the nervous system, is significantly higher in multiples than in singletons. Very few studies have compared each type of birth defect after ART between singletons and multiples. Therefore, the birth defect findings in spontaneous pregnancies or other pregnancies, neither of which were stratified by ART status, are described below. However, caution is again needed given that ART usually produces dizygotic twins, who tend to have a better pre- and perinatal outcome than monozygotic twins. The difference between singletons and multiples may be diminished in ART subjects.

Many studies (Doyle et al., 1991; Glinianaia et al., 2008; Klemetti et al., 2005; Mastroiacovo et al., 1999; Ramos-Arroyo, 1991; Tang et al., 2006) have reported a higher proportion of birth defects of the nervous system in twins or multiples compared to singletons. Live births with anencephaly were all multiples in the present study. Anencephaly is frequently reported to be higher in twins/multiples than in singletons (Doyle et al., 1991; Li et al., 2003; Tang et al., 2006).

A higher proportion of PDA in multiples are frequently observed (Layde et al., 1980; Li et al., 2003; Tang et al., 2006), and is attributed to the prematurity or shorter gestational age of multiples (Li et al., 2003; Pinborg et al., 2004b). According to Pinborg et al. (2004b), after the exclusion of PDA, which is strongly associated with preterm birth, no significant differences in any malformation rates were observed between twins and singletons. PDA was also frequently seen among multiples in the present study, and the RRs of any birth defects per pregnancy and of any birth defects per live birth both decreased when this disease was excluded.

3) Limitations

This study has the following limitations, most of which could be attributed to the dataset; namely, the fact that individual information was obtained only from the subjects with birth defects after ART, not the total ART pregnancies.

The first and greatest limitation is that the author could not check the reliability of the data directly. Several misspellings or misclassifications of diseases were found in the annual report. This is the essential limitation of secondary data analyses. Second, although the present dataset was from a multi-year, nationwide survey, it still did not have sufficiently high enough statistical power to detect the statistical significance of several diseases with high RR. Third, the prevalences of birth defects per live birth were underestimated in singletons, and, on the other hand, they were overestimated in multiples according to the present definition of live births.

Thus, the RRs per live birth were logically overestimated. Fourth, the author could not control for confounding factors that can affect ART and/or birth defects (Källén et al., 2005, 2010), such as maternal age, parity, smoking, and socioeconomic status, medical history, and prenatal care, since this data on the general ART populations were not available. However, to date, many studies have not necessarily controlled for confounding factors (Hansen et al., 2005). Fifth, follow-up after birth was limited to the early neonatal period, and was incomplete, especially for singletons. Some birth defects are not obvious within a few days after birth. Sixth, all methods of ART (e.g., IVF, ICSI and so on) were treated as ART. Regarding this point, a recent meta-analysis (Lie et al., 2005) and national study (Bonduelle et al., 2002) reported that the ICSI procedure represents no significant additional risks of major birth defects in addition to the risks involved in standard IVF. The other limitations are the same as those pointed out by many studies related to birth defects (Doyle et al., 1991; Glinianaia et al., 2008; Goel et al., 2009; Reefhuis et al., 2009; Zhang et al., 2011); namely, ascertainment bias (both over-ascertainment and under-ascertainment in multiples), the classification or diagnosis, no data on zygosity or the chorionicity of multiples.

Even with all these limitations, the present results overviewed the current situation of births defects after ART according to plurality. The risk of birth defects in ART live births is not significantly different between multiples and singletons, while the risk per pregnancy is clearly higher in multiple births. In conclusion, the overall impact of birth defects after ART would be larger in families with multiples, since the mean number of children would be larger in these families compared to in families without multiples. ART might contribute to the risk of birth defects both directly, by increasing the risk of defects among singletons, and indirectly by increasing the occurrence of twinning (Mastroiacovo et al., 1999). Proper follow-up for all families after ART, especially for families with multiple pregnancies/births, is needed.

2. Concordance and Discordance

1) Method of Analysis

A correct zygosity diagnosis is rare in most studies of birth defects. Researchers have often compared resemblance between same-sex pairs (as a proxy for MZ pairs) and opposite-sex DZ pairs, on the assumption that there is no sex difference in prevalence. In the present study, information was obtained only from probands. In such a situation, the probandwise concordance rate is the second-best measure of resemblance in twin pairs.

Although most subjects in the present study were DZ pairs, some MZ pairs may well have also been included. According to a recent meta-analysis by Vitthala et al, (2009), the incidence of MZ twins after ART is 2.25 times that after natural conception. Caution is warranted in interpreting these values because most previous studies used the pairwise rather than the probandwise concordance rate. Ascertainment bias in the identification of twin pairs would be small in the present sample, since birth defects during pregnancy or the neonatal period (at the latest) were reported in the same hospital. However, this ascertainment period may underestimate the concordance rate if pairs differed in the age when symptoms of birth defects became obvious.

2) Concordance or Discordance of Birth Defects in Twin Pairs

The number of concordant pairs was clearly higher for male–male pairs than for female–female and opposite-sex pairs. No previous study reported that concordance rates differed according to the sex combination of twin pairs.

The concordance rate for any birth defect is higher in MZ pairs and all twin pairs as compared with DZ pairs and opposite-sex DZ pairs, (Campana and Roubicek, 1996; Imaizumi et al., 1990; Kato and Fujiki, 1992; Myrianthopoulos, 1976) respectively, which suggests a genetic contribution to birth defects. The probandwise concordance rate of any birth defect (9.6%) was similar to the estimated recurrence risk among sib-pairs (9.0%) and was much higher than the prevalence in the general population (0.81%). These results suggest familial aggregation of birth defects and that the origin of this aggregation is multifactorial inheritance.

The probandwise concordance rate of congenital malformations of the circulatory system was 30-fold higher than the prevalence in the general population. Kenna et al. (1975) found 2 concordant pairs out of 15 MZ pairs and 2 concordant pairs with different heart lesions out of DZ 12 pairs. According to Hardin et al. (2009) the probandwise concordance rate for opposite-sex DZ twin pairs was 14.0%. A small number of studies directly compared the recurrence risk of twin pairs with that of first-degree relatives. Caputo et al. (2005) compared the recurrence risk in DZ pairs and sib-pairs and concluded that the higher recurrence and concordance of congenital heart disease in DZ twins might depend on a poorly understood environmental risk during pregnancy. However, Øyen et al. (2009) found that intrauterine conditions had no effect, after comparing the RRRs of opposite-sex twin pairs and first-degree relatives.

It has been suggested that patent ductus arteriosus (PDA) is related to prematurity and is consequently more prevalent in twins (Bergh et al., 1999; Källén, 1986; Pinborg et al., 2004a). Layde et al. (1980) found that a high concordance rate was observed in same-sex pairs, which suggests both a strong genetic component to the etiology of PDA and high rates of prematurity in twin pairs. The present finding of a high concordance rate and RRR (=445) for PDA supports the genetic/shared environmental hypothesis. When concordance rates were calculated after excluding PDA cases, the results were not markedly different, as shown in Table 6.

Regarding congenital malformations of the nervous system in twins, neural tube defects have been well examined (Campana et al., 1996; Deak et al., 2008; Imaizumi, 1978, 1989; Imaizumi et al., 1990; Janerick and Piper, 1978; Rogers, 1976; Windham and Sever, 1982). The present study observed no concordant pair with anencephalus, spina bifida, or hydrocephalus. There were 2 male–male concordant pairs with lissencephaly (subcategory Q04), but no other such cases among twins or singletons, suggesting that the original data was incorrectly inputted.

One male–male concordant pair showed both micrognathia and low-set ear (subcategory Q17). There is no population-based twin study with these defects.

There was one male–male concordant pair who had cleft palate with cleft lip (subcategory Q37), with a 14.3% probandwise concordance rate. This value is similar to that of DZ pairs (16.7%), as reported by Lin et al. (1999) According to Grosen et al. (2011) the probandwise concordance rate for the cleft lip/cleft palate was higher for MZ pairs than for DZ pairs. However, they also found that the recurrence risk for both types of clefts was greater in DZ twins than in non-twin siblings, suggesting intrauterine environmental effects on these traits. The fact that the RRR (=499) for a cleft palate with cleft lip was highest in the present study supports their results.

There was no concordant pair with esophageal atresia (subcategory Q39). David and O'Callaghan (1975) found that the probandwise concordance rate for this condition was 19.0%, although Orford et al. (2000) reported a low pairwise concordance rate (4.1%). There was 1 concordant opposite-sex DZ pair with an imperforate anus (subcategory Q42). Källén (1986) reported that for alimentary atresia, including imperforate anus, concordance was rather common among same-sex pairs.

There was 1 concordant opposite-sex DZ pair with brachymelia (subcategory Q73). Métneki et al. (1996) studied the occurrence of congenital limb reduction defects in twins and concluded that genetic factors have a limited role in pathogenesis. Pober et al. (2005) conducted a large twin study associated with Bochdalek diaphragmatic hernia, including 8 twin cases with no concordant pairs.

The concordance rate of congenital malformations and deformations of the musculoskeletal system was low in the present study, in contrast to the relatively high prevalence among the general population.

3) Limitations

Most limitations of this study are due to deficiencies in the data collection system. The first limitation was the lack of a zygosity classification for same-sex pairs. Second, the pairing of twins was not necessarily complete. Some concordant pairs might not have been real twin pairs. Third, the statistical power of the analyses was limited. The present concordance rates might be strongly influenced by chance factors, since most disease concordance rates were calculated on the basis of no or 1 concordant pair.

4) Multiple Births After ART

The increased risk of adverse outcomes in ART multiples/twins is not limited to an adverse neonatal outcome. ART twins are more likely to develop cerebral palsy and be hospitalized than ART singletons (Ericson et al., 2002; Stromberg et al., 2002). According to the questionnaire survey by Pinborg et al. (2003b), speech development and physical health up to 4 years of age were significantly worse in twins than in singletons, and twins were more likely to have special needs and require surgical interventions than singletons. Maternal risks increased in ART twin pregnancies, as the women were more likely to be on sick leave and hospitalized during pregnancy (Pinborg et al., 2004c).

These adverse outcomes of twin pregnancy after ART promoted an eSET policy for ART (Gordts et al., 2005; Hazekamp et al., 2000). While ART multiples decreased dramatically after 2006 in Japan, long-term social, as well as medical, follow-up for mothers of multiples and the multiples themselves were rarely performed. A standardized methodology of follow-up studies after ART should be established (Woldringh et al., 2010). Considering the medical and social impacts of multiple births (Bryan et al., 1997; Ooki, 2009), there is an urgent need for a hospital-based monitoring system for fertility treatments, including not only ART, but non-ART treatment, and multiple births in Japan. Moreover, effective record linkage between data on fertility treatments, birth defects and vital statistics is essential.

CONCLUSION

The present study clarified that although the multiple births rate has been decreasing after 2005, the overall rapid increase in the real number of multiple births and multiple-birth rate in the past thirty years in Japan could mainly be due to iatrogenic, not spontaneous, multiple births of mothers with advanced age. In other words, the effect of higher maternal age appears more in the number of iatrogenic multiples, not in an increase of spontaneous dizygotic twinning. The present study also demonstrated that in contrast to the recent rapid decrease of ART multiple births, the relative impact of non-ART iatrogenic multiples, especially twins, is increasing and should not be overlooked. The relationship between the SET rate and the multiple pregnancy rate seemed near the reverse sigmoid curve, with an almost linear reduction of the multiple pregnancy rate in the period without a large decrease of the total pregnancy rate. The estimated MZ twinning rate after SET was around 2%. These results are useful for the evaluation of the total effects of the SET policy on fertility treatment.

The risk of birth defects in ART live births is not significantly different between multiples and singletons, but the impact of birth defects after ART would be larger in families with multiples, since the mean number of children would be larger in these families compared to families with singletons. The present results also provide a good overview of concordance rates among twin pairs with birth defects after ART. Strong familial aggregation was observed for some birth defects.

Proper follow-up for all families, especially for families with multiple pregnancies/births, after ART is needed.

ACKNOWLEDGMENTS

I would like to thank Toshimi Ooma for assistance with data analysis. This work was supported in part by a Grant-in-Aid for Scientific Research (B) (Grant Number 24390167) and Grant-in-Aid for Challenging Exploratory Research (Grant Number 23659356) from the Japan Society for the Promotion of Science.

REFERENCES

Basso, O., Nohr, E. A., Christensen, K., and Olsen, J. (2004). Risk of twinning as a function of maternal height and body mass index. *JAMA, 291*, 1564-1566.

Bergh, T., Ericson, A., Hillensjö, T., Nygren, K. G., and Wennerholm, U. B. (1999). Deliveries and children born after in-vitro fertilisation in Sweden 1982-95: a retrospective cohort study. *Lancet, 354*, 1579-1585.

Blickstein, I., Verhoeven, H. C. and Keith, L. G. (1999). Zygotic splitting after assisted reproduction, *N. Engl. J. Med., 340*, 738-739.

Blickstein, I., Jones, C., and Keith, L. G. (2003). Zygotic-splitting rates after single-embryo transfers in in vitro fertilization. *N. Engl. J. Med., 348*, 2366-2367.

Bolton, P., Yamashita, Y., and Farquhar, C. M. (2003). Role of fertility treatments in multiple pregnancy at National Women's Hospital from 1996 to 2001. *Aust. N. Z. J. Obstet. Gynaecol., 43*, 364-368.

Bonduelle, M., Liebaers, I., Deketelaere, V., Derde, M. P., Camus, M., Devroey, P., et al. (2002). Neonatal data on a cohort of 2889 infants born after ICSI (1991-1999) and of 2995 infants born after IVF (1983-1999). *Hum. Reprod., 17*, 671-694.

Bonduelle, M., Wennerholm, U. B., Loft, A., Tarlatzis, B. C., Peters, C., Henriet, S., et al. (2005). A multi-centre cohort study of the physical health of 5-year-old children conceived after intracytoplasmic sperm injection, in vitro fertilization and natural conception. *Hum. Reprod., 20*, 413-419.

Bortolus, R., Parazzini, F., Chatenoud, L., Benzi, G., Bianchi, M. M., and Marini, A. (1999). The epidemiology of multiple births. *Hum. Reprod. Update, 5,* 179-187.

Boulet, S. L., Schieve, L. A., Nannini, A., Ferre, C., Devine, O., Cohen, B., et al. (2008). Perinatal outcomes of twin births conceived using assisted reproduction technology: a population-based study. *Hum. Reprod., 23,* 1941-1948.

Bryan, E., Denton, J., and Hallett, F. (1997). *Guidelines for Professionals: Multiple Pregnancy,* London: Multiple Births Foundation.

Bulmer, M. G. (1959). The effect of parental age, parity and duration of marriage on the twinning rate. *Ann. Hum. Genet. 23,* 454-458.

Callahan, T. L., and Greene, M. F. (1998).The economic impact of multiple gestation. *Infertility and Reproductive Medical Clinics of North America, 9,* 513-525.

Campana, M. A., and Roubicek, M. M. (1996). Maternal and neonatal variables in twins: an epidemiological approach. *Acta Genet. Med. Gemellol. (Roma), 45,* 461-469.

Caputo, S., Russo, M. G., Capozzi, G., Morelli, C., Argiento, P., Di Salvo, G., et al. (2005). Congenital heart disease in a population of dizygotic twins: an echocardiographic study. *Int. J. Cardiol.,* 102, 293-296.

Chang, H. J., Lee, J. R., Jee, B. C., Suh, C. S., and Kim, S. H. (2009). Impact of blastocyst transfer on offspring sex ratio and the monozygotic twinning rate: a systematic review and meta-analysis, *Fertil. Steril., 91,* 2381-2390.

Chen, B. Y., Hwang, B. F., and Guo, Y. L. (2009). Epidemiology of congenital anomalies in a population-based birth registry in Taiwan, 2002. *J. Formos. Med. Assoc., 108,* 460-468.

Coetsier, T., and Dhont, M. (1998). Avoiding multiple pregnancies in in-vitro fertilization: who's afraid of single embryo transfer? *Hum. Reprod., 13,* 2663-2664.

Corchia, C., Mastroiacovo, P., Lanni, R., Mannazzu, R., Currò, V., and Fabris, C. (1996). What proportion of multiple births are due to ovulation induction? A register-based study in Italy. *Am. J. Public Health, 86,* 851-854.

David, T. J., and O'Callaghan, S. E. (1975). Oesophageal atresia in the South West of England. *J. Med. Genet., 12,* 1-11.

Deak, K. L., Siegel, D. G., George, T. M., Gregory, S., Ashley-Koch, A., Speer, M. C. ; NTD Collaborative Group. (2008). Further evidence for a maternal genetic effect and a sex-influenced effect contributing to risk for human neural tube defects. *Birth Defects Res. A Clin. Mol. Teratol., 82,* 662-669.

De Neubourg, D., and Gerris, J. (2006). What about the remaining twins since single-embryo transfer? How far can (should) we go? *Hum. Reprod., 21,* 843-846.

De Sutter, P., Van der Elst, J., Coetsier, T., and Dhont, M. (2003). Single embryo transfer and multiple pregnancy rate reduction in IVF/ICSI: a 5-year appraisal, *Reprod. Biomed. Online, 6,* 464-469.

Denton, J. (2005). Twins and more--2. Practical aspects of parenting in the early years. *J. Fam. Health Care, 15,* 173-176.

Derom, C., Vlietinck, R., Derom, R., Van den Berghe, H., and Thiery, M. (1987). Increased monozygotic twinning rate after ovulation induction, *Lancet, 1,* 1236-1238.

Derom, C., Derom, R., Vlietinck, R., Maes, H., and Van den Berghe, H. (1993). Iatrogenic multiple pregnancies in East Flanders, Belgium. *Fertil. Steril., 60,* 493-496.

Doyle, P. E., Beral, V., Botting, B., and Wale, C. J. (1991). Congenital malformation in twins in England and Wales. *J. Epidemiol. Community Health, 45,* 43-48.

Edwards, J. H. (1960). The simulation of mendelism. *Acta Genet. Stat. Med., 10,* 63-70.

Ericson, A., and Källén, B. (2001). Congenital malformations in infants born after IVF: a population-based study. *Hum. Reprod., 16,* 504-509.

Ericson, A., Nygren, K. G., Olausson, P. O., and Källén, B. (2002). Hospital care utilization of infants born after IVF. *Hum. Reprod., 17,* 929-932.

Fauser, B. C., Devroey, P., and Macklon, N. S. (2005). Multiple birth resulting from ovarian stimulation for subfertility treatment. *Lancet, 365,*1807-1816.

Fujii, M., Matsuoka, R., Bergel, E., van der Poel, S., and Okai, T. (2010). Perinatal risk in singleton pregnancies after in vitro fertilization. *Fertil. Steril., 94,* 2113-2117.

Fuster, V., Zuluaga, P., Colantonio, S., and de Blas, C. (2008). Factors associated with recent increase of multiple births in Spain. *Twin Res. Hum. Genet., 11,* 70-76.

Gelbaya, T. A., Tsoumpou, I, and Nardo, L. G. (2010). The likelihood of live birth and multiple birth after single versus double embryo transfer at the cleavage stage: a systematic review and meta-analysis. *Fertil. Steril., 94,* 936-945.

Ghai, V., and Vidyasagar, D. (1988). Morbidity and mortality factors in twins. An epidemiologic approach. *Clin. Perinatol., 15,* 123-140.

Glinianaia, S. V., Rankin, J., and Wright, C. (2008). Congenital anomalies in twins: a register-based study. *Hum. Reprod., 23,* 1306-1311.

Goel, A., Sreenivas, V., Bhatnagar, S., Lodha, R., and Bhatla, N. (2009). Risk of birth defects increased in pregnancies conceived by assisted human reproduction. *Fertil. Steril., 92,* e7.

Gordts, S., Campo, R., Puttemans, P., Brosens, I., Valkenburg, M., Norre, J., et al. (2005). Belgian legislation and the effect of elective single embryo transfer on IVF outcome. *Reprod. Biomed. Online, 10,* 436-441.

Grosen, D., Bille, C., Petersen, I., Skytthe, A., Hjelmborg, Jv., Pedersen, J. K., et al. (2011). Risk of oral clefts in twins. *Epidemiology, 22,* 313-319.

Guo, S. W. (1998). Inflation of sibling recurrence-risk ratio, due to ascertainment bias and/or overreporting. *Am. J. Hum. Genet., 63,* 252-258.

Hall, J. G. (2003). Twinning. *Lancet, 362,* 735-743.

Hall, J. E., and Callahan, T. L. (2005). Economic Considerations. In Blickstein, I., and Keith, L. G. (Eds.), *Multiple Pregnancy: Epidemiology, Gestation and Perinatal Outcome.* (2th ed. pp.889-894). UK: Informa Healthcare.

Hamberger, L., Hardarson, T., and Nygren, K. G. (2005). Avoidance of multiple pregnancy by use of single embryo transfer. *Minerva Ginecol., 57,* 15-19.

Hansen, M., Bower, C., Milne, E., de Klerk, N., and Kurinczuk, J. J. (2005). Assisted reproductive technologies and the risk of birth defects --a systematic review. *Hum. Reprod., 20,* 328-338.

Hardin, J., Carmichael, S. L., Selvin, S., Lammer, E. J., and Shaw, G. M. (2009). Increased prevalence of cardiovascular defects among 56,709 California twin pairs. *Am. J. Med. Genet. A, 149A,* 877-886.

Hazekamp, J., Bergh, C., Wennerholm, U. B., Hovatta, O., Karlström, P. O., and Selbing, A. (2000). Avoiding multiple pregnancies in ART: consideration of new strategies. *Hum. Reprod., 15,* 1217-1219.

Helmerhorst, F. M., Perquin, D. A., Donker, D., and Keirse, M. J. (2004). Perinatal outcome of singletons and twins after assisted conception: a systematic review of controlled studies. *BMJ, 328,* 261.

Hoekstra, C., Zhao, Z. Z., Lambalk, C. B., Willemsen, G., Martin, N. G., Boomsma, D. I., et al. (2008). Dizygotic twinning. *Hum. Reprod. Update, 14,* 37-47.

Hoekstra, C., Willemsen, G., van Beijsterveldt, C. E., Lambalk, C. B., Montgomery, G. W., and Boomsma, D. I. (2010). Body composition, smoking, and spontaneous dizygotic twinning. *Fertil. Steril., 93,* 885-893.

Imaizumi, Y. (1978). Concordance and discordance of anencephaly in 109 twin pairs in Japan. *Jinrui Idengaku Zasshi, 23,* 389-393.

Imaizumi, Y. (1989). Concordance and discordance of congenital hydrocephalus in 107 twin pairs in Japan. *Teratology, 40,* 101-103.

Imaizumi, Y., Asaka, A., and Inouye, E. (1990). Fetal deaths with birth defects among Japanese multiples, 1974. *Acta Genet. Med. Gemellol. (Roma), 39,* 345-350.

Imaizumi, Y., and Inouye, E. (1979). Analysis of multiple birth rates in Japan. 1. Secular trend, maternal age effect, and geographical variation in twinning rates. *Acta Genet. Med. Gemellol. (Roma), 28,* 107-124.

Jackson, R. A., Gibson, K. A., Wu, Y. W., and Croughan, M. S. (2004). Perinatal outcomes in singletons following in vitro fertilization: a meta-analysis. *Obstet. Gynecol., 103,* 551-563.

Janerich, D. T., and Piper, J. (1978). Shifting genetic patterns in anencephaly and spina bifida. *J. Med. Genet., 15,* 101-105.

Jones, H. W. Jr. (2007). Iatrogenic multiple births: a 2003 checkup. *Fertil. Steril., 87,* 453-455.

Joy, J., McClure, N., and Cooke, I. E. (2008). A comparison of spontaneously conceived twins and twins conceived by artificial reproductive technologies. *J. Obstet. Gynaecol., 28,* 580-585.

Källén, B. (1986). Congenital malformations in twins: a population study. *Acta Genet. Med. Gemellol. (Roma), 35,* 167-178.

Källén, B., Finnström, O., Nygren, K. G., and Olausson, P. O. (2005). In vitro fertilization (IVF) in Sweden: risk for congenital malformations after different IVF methods. *Birth Defects Res. A Clin. Mol. Teratol., 73,* 162-169.

Källén, B., Finnström, O., Lindam, A., Nilsson, E., Nygren, K. G., and Otterblad, P. O. (2010). Congenital malformations in infants born after in vitro fertilization in Sweden. *Birth Defects Res. A Clin. Mol. Teratol., 88,* 137-143.

Kaprio, J., and Marttila, R. (2005). Demographic trends in Nordic countries. In Blickstein, I., and Keith, L. G. (Eds.), *Multiple Pregnancy: Epidemiology, Gestation and Perinatal Outcome* (2th ed. pp.22-25). UK: Informa Healthcare.

Kato, K., and Fujiki, K. (1992). Multiple births and congenital anomalies in Tokyo Metropolitan Hospitals, 1979-1990. *Acta Genet. Med. Gemellol. (Roma), 41,* 253-259.

Kawachiya, S., Bodri, D., Shimada, N., Kato, K., Takehara, Y., and Kato, O. (2011). Blastocyst culture is associated with an elevated incidence of monozygotic twinning after single embryo transfer. *Fertil. Steril., 95,* 2140-2142.

Kenna, A. P., Smithells, R. W., and Fielding, D. W. (1975). *Congenital heart disease in Liverpool:* 1960--69. Q J Med, 44, 17-44.

Klemetti, R., Gissler, M., Sevón, T., Koivurova, S., Ritvanen, A., and Hemminki, E. (2005). Children born after assisted fertilization have an increased rate of major congenital anomalies. *Fertil. Steril., 84,* 1300-1307.

Knopman, J., Krey, L. C., Lee, J., Fino, M. E., Novetsky, A. P., and Noyes, N. (2010). Monozygotic twinning: an eight-year experience at a large IVF center. *Fertil. Steril., 94,* 502-510.

Kresowik, J. D., Stegmann, B. J., Sparks, A. E., Ryan, G. L., and van Voorhis, B. J. (2011). Five-years of a mandatory single-embryo transfer (mSET) policy dramatically reduces twinning rate without lowering pregnancy rates. *Fertil. Steril., 96,* 1367-1369.

Layde, P. M., Erickson, J. D., Falek, A., and McCarthy, B. J. (1980). Congenital malformation in twins. *Am. J. Hum. Genet., 32,* 69-78.

Li, S. J., Ford, N., Meister, K., and Bodurtha, J. (2003). Increased risk of birth defects among children from multiple births. *Birth Defects Res. A Clin. Mol. Teratol., 67,* 879-885.

Lie, R. T., Lyngstadaas, A., Ørstavik, K. H., Bakketeig, L. S., Jacobsen, G., and Tanbo, T. (2005). Birth defects in children conceived by ICSI compared with children conceived by other IVF-methods; a meta-analysis. *Int. J. Epidemiol., 34,* 696-701.

Lin, Y. C., Lo, L. J., Noordhoff, M. S., and Chen, Y. R. (1999). Cleft of the lip and palate in twins. *Changgeng Yi Xue Za Zhi, 22,* 61-67.

Little, J., and Nevin, N. C. (1989). Congenital anomalies in twins in Northern Ireland. I: Anomalies in general and specific anomalies other than neural tube defects and of the cardiovascular system, 1974-1979. *Acta Genet. Med. Gemellol. (Roma), 38,* 1-16.

Luke, B., and Keith, L. G. (1990). Monozygotic twinning as a congenital defect and congenital defects in monozygotic twins. *Fetal Diagn. Ther., 5,* 61-69.

MacDorman, M. F., Martin, J. A., Mathews, T. J., Hoyert, D. L., and Ventura, S. J. (2005). Explaining the 2001-02 infant mortality increase: data from the linked birth/infant death data set. *Natl. Vital. Stat. Rep.*, 53, 1-22.

Macfarlane, A., and Blondel, B. (2005). Demographic trends in Western European countries. In Blickstein, I., and Keith, L. G. (Eds.), *Multiple Pregnancy: Epidemiology, Gestation and Perinatal Outcome* (2th ed. pp.11-21). UK: Informa Healthcare.

Martin, J. A., Hamilton, B. E., Sutton, P. D., Ventura, S. J., Menacker, F., Kirmeyer, S., et al. (2007). Births: final data for 2005. *Natl. Vital Stat. Rep., 56,* 1-103.

Mastroiacovo, P., Castilla, E. E., Arpino, C., Botting, B., Cocchi, G., Goujard, J., et al. (1999). Congenital malformations in twins: an international study. *Am. J. Med. Genet., 83,* 117-124.

Mayor, S. (2010). Risk of congenital malformations in children born after assisted reproduction is higher than previously thought. *BMJ, 340,* c3191.

McGue, M. (1992). When assessing twin concordance, use the probandwise not the pairwise rate. *Schizophr. Bull., 18,* 171-176.

Métneki, J., Czeizel, A. E., and Evans, J. A. (1996). Congenital limb reduction defects in twins. *Eur. J. Pediatr.,* 155, 483-490.

Milne, P., Cottell, E., Allen, C., Spillane, H., Vasallo, J., and Wingfield, M. (2010). Reducing twin pregnancy rates after IVF--elective single embryo transfer (eSET). *Ir. Med. J., 103,* 9-11.

Moayeri, S. E., Behr, B., Lathi, R. B., Westphal, L. M., and Milki, A. A. (2007). Risk of monozygotic twinning with blastocyst transfer decreases over time: an 8-year experience. *Fertil. Steril., 87,* 1028-1032.

Myrianthopoulos, N. C. (1976). Congenital malformations in twins. *Acta Genet. Med. Gemellol. (Roma), 25,* 331-335.

Nylander, P. P. (1981). The factors that influence twinning rates. *Acta Genet. Med. Gemellol. (Roma), 30,* 189-202.

Ooki, S. (2006). Population-based database of multiples in childhood of Ishikawa Prefecture, Japan. *Twin Res. Hum. Genet., 9,* 832-837.

Ooki, S. (2009). Chapter12. Strategy and practice of support for multiple birth families: Evidence-based care and population approach with human network. In Pacey, H. Krause, and Tahlia, M. Dailey. (Eds.), *Handbook of Parenting: Styles, Stresses, and Strategies* (pp.175-239). NY: Nova Science Publishers.

Ooki, S. (2010a). The effect of an increase in the rate of multiple births on low-birth-weight and preterm deliveries during 1975-2008. *J. Epidemiol., 20,* 480-488.

Ooki, S. (2010b). Re: "Estimation of the contribution of non-assisted reproductive technology ovulation stimulation fertility treatments to US singleton and multiple births". *Am. J. Epidemiol., 172,* 981-982.

Ooki, S. (2011a). Estimation of the contribution of assisted and non-assisted reproductive technology fertility treatments to multiple births during the past 30 years in Japan: 1979-2008. *Twin Res. Hum. Genet., 14,* 476-483.

Ooki, S. (2011b). Effect of maternal age and fertility treatment on the increase in multiple births in Japan: vital statistics, 1974-2009. *J. Epidemiol., 21,* 507-511.

Ooki, S. (2011c). Birth defects in singleton versus multiple ART births in Japan (2004-2008). *J. Pregnancy, 2011,* 285706.

Ooki, S. (2012a). Theoretical model of the relationship between single embryo transfer rate and multiple pregnancy rate in Japan. *J. Pregnancy, 2012,* 620753.

Ooki, S. (2012b). Birth defects after assisted reproductive technology in Japan: Comparison between multiples and singletons, 2004-2009. *Reprod. Sys. Sexual Disorders, 2012,* S:5.

Ooki, S. (2012c). Concordance rates of birth defects after assisted reproductive technology among 17,258 Japanese twin pregnancies: A nationwide survey, 2004–2009, *J. Epidemiol.,* doi:10.2188/jea.JE20120103.

Orford, J., Glasson, M., Beasley, S., Shi, E., Myers, N., and Cass, D. (2000). Oesophageal atresia in twins. *Pediatr. Surg. Int., 16,* 541-545.

Øyen, N., Poulsen, G., Boyd, H. A., Wohlfahrt, J., Jensen, P. K., and Melbye, M. (2009). Recurrence of congenital heart defects in families. *Circulation,* 120, 295-301.

Papanikolaou, E. G., Fatemi, H., Venetis, C., Donoso, P., Kolibianakis, E., Tournaye, H., et al. (2010). Monozygotic twinning is not increased after single blastocyst transfer compared with single cleavage-stage embryo transfer. *Fertil. Steril., 93,* 592-597.

Park, Y. S., Choi, S. H., Shim, K. S., Chang, J. Y., Hahn, W. H., Choi, Y. S., et al. (2010). Multiple births conceived by assisted reproductive technology in Korea. *Korean J. Pediatr., 53,* 880-885.

Pharoah, P. O. (2002). Neurological outcome in twins. *Semin. Neonatol., 7,* 223-230.

Pinborg, A., Loft, A., Schmidt, L., and Andersen, A. N. (2003a). Attitudes of IVF/ICSI-twin mothers towards twins and single embryo transfer. *Hum. Reprod., 18,* 621-627.

Pinborg, A., Loft, A., Schmidt, L., and Andersen, A. N. (2003b). Morbidity in a Danish national cohort of 472 IVF/ICSI twins, 1132 non-IVF/ICSI twins and 634 IVF/ICSI singletons: health-related and social implications for the children and their families. *Hum. Reprod., 18,* 1234-1243.

Pinborg, A., Loft, A., Rasmussen, S., Schmidt, L., Langhoff-Roos, J., Greisen, G., et al. (2004a). Neonatal outcome in a Danish national cohort of 3438 IVF/ICSI and 10,362 non-IVF/ICSI twins born between 1995 and 2000. *Hum. Reprod., 19,* 435-441.

Pinborg, A., Loft, A., and Nyboe Andersen, A. (2004b). Neonatal outcome in a Danish national cohort of 8602 children born after in vitro fertilization or intracytoplasmic sperm injection: the role of twin pregnancy. *Acta Obstet. Gynecol. Scand., 83,* 1071-1078.

Pinborg, A., Loft, A., Schmidt, L., Langhoff-Roos, J., and Andersen, A. N. (2004c). Maternal risks and perinatal outcome in a Danish national cohort of 1005 twin pregnancies: the role of in vitro fertilization. *Acta Obstet. Gynecol. Scand., 83,* 75-84.

Pober, B. R., Lin, A., Russell, M., Ackerman, K. G., Chakravorty, S., Strauss, B., et al. (2005). Infants with Bochdalek diaphragmatic hernia: sibling precurrence and monozygotic twin discordance in a hospital-based malformation surveillance program. *Am. J. Med. Genet. A, 138A,* 81-88.

Ramos-Arroyo, M. A. (1991). Birth defects in twins: study in a Spanish population. *Acta Genet. Med. Gemellol. (Roma), 40,* 337-344.

Reddy, U. M., Branum, A. M., and Klebanoff, M. A. (2005). Relationship of maternal body mass index and height to twinning. *Obstet. Gynecol., 105,* 593-597.

Reefhuis, J., Honein, M. A., Schieve, L. A., Correa, A., Hobbs, C. A., Rasmussen, S. A., et al. (2009). Assisted reproductive technology and major structural birth defects in the United States. *Hum. Reprod., 24,* 360-366.

Rimm, A. A., Katayama, A. C., Diaz, M., and Katayama, K. P. (2004). A meta-analysis of controlled studies comparing major malformation rates in IVF and ICSI infants with naturally conceived children. *J. Assist. Reprod. Genet.,* 21, 437-443.

Rogers, S. C. (1976). Anencephalus, Spina Bifida, twins, and teratoma. *Br. J. Prev. Soc. Med., 30,* 26-28.

Saito, H., Tsutsumi, O., Noda, Y., Ibuki, Y., and Hiroi, M. (2000). Do assisted reproductive technologies have effects on the demography of monozygotic twinning? *Fertil. Steril., 74,* 178-179.

Schieve, L. A., Devine, O., Boyle, C. A., Petrini, J. R., and Warner, L. (2009). Estimation of the contribution of non-assisted reproductive technology ovulation stimulation fertility treatments to US singleton and multiple births. *Am. J. Epidemiol., 170,* 1396-1407.

Scholz, T., Bartholomäus, S., Grimmer, I., Kentenich, H., and Obladen, M. (1999). Problems of multiple births after ART: medical, psychological, social and financial aspects. *Hum. Reprod., 14,* 2932-2937.

Scotland, G. S., McLernon, D., Kurinczuk, J. J., McNamee, P., Harrild, K., Lyall, H., et al. (2011). Minimising twins in in vitro fertilisation: a modelling study assessing the costs, consequences and cost-utility of elective single versus double embryo transfer over a 20-year time horizon. *BJOG, 118,* 1073-1083.

Sharara, F. I., and Abdo, G. (2010). Incidence of monozygotic twins in blastocyst and cleavage stage assisted reproductive technology cycles. *Fertil. Steril., 93,* 642-645.

Shebl, O., Ebner, T., Sir, A., Sommergruber, M., and Tews, G. (2009). The role of mode of conception in the outcome of twin pregnancies. *Minerva Ginecol.,* 61, 141-152.

Stromberg, B., Dahlquist, G., Ericson, A., Finnstrom, O., Koster, M., and Stjernqvist, K. (2002). Neurological sequelae in children born after in-vitro fertilisation: a population-based study. *Lancet, 359,* 461-465.

Sunde, A. (2007). Significant reduction of twins with single embryo transfer in IVF. *Reprod. Biomed. Online, 15,* 28-34.

Tandberg, A., Bjørge, T., Børdahl, P. E., and Skjaerven, R. (2007). Increasing twinning rates in Norway, 1967-2004: the influence of maternal age and assisted reproductive technology (ART). *Acta Obstet. Gynecol. Scand., 86,* 833-839.

Tang, Y., Ma, C. X., Cui, W., Chang, V., Ariet, M., Morse, S. B., et al. (2006). The risk of birth defects in multiple births: a population-based study. *Matern. Child Health J., 10,* 75-81.

Tanimura, M., Matsui, I., and Kobayashi, N. (1990). Child abuse of one of a pair of twins in Japan. *Lancet, 336,* 1298-1299.

Thorpe, K., Golding, J., MacGillivray, I., and Greenwood, R. (1991). Comparison of prevalence of depression in mothers of twins and mothers of singletons. *BMJ, 302,* 875-878.

Van Royen, E., Mangelschots, K., De Neubourg, D., Valkenburg, M., Van de Meerssche, M., Ryckaert, G., et al. (1999). Characterization of a top quality embryo, a step towards single-embryo transfer. *Hum. Reprod., 14,* 2345-2349.

Verpoest, W., Van Landuyt, L., Desmyttere, S., Cremers, A., Devroey, P., and Liebaers, I. (2009). The incidence of monozygotic twinning following PGD is not increased. *Hum. Reprod., 24,* 2945-2950.

Vitthala, S., Gelbaya, T. A., Brison, D. R., Fitzgerald, C. T., and Nardo, L. G. (2009). The risk of monozygotic twins after assisted reproductive technology: a systematic review and meta-analysis. *Hum. Reprod. Update, 15,* 45-55.

Wenstrom, K. D., Syrop, C. H., Hammitt, D. G., and Van Voorhis, B. J. (1993). Increased risk of monochorionic twinning associated with assisted reproduction. *Fertil. Steril., 60,* 510-514.

Williams, C., and Sutcliffe, A. (2009). Infant outcomes of assisted reproduction. *Early Hum. Dev., 85,* 673-677.

Williams, C., Sutcliffe, A., and Sebire, N. J. (2010). Congenital malformations after assisted reproduction: risks and implications for prenatal diagnosis and fetal medicine. *Ultrasound Obstet. Gynecol., 35,* 255-259.

Windham, G. C., and Sever, L. E. (1982). Neural tube defects among twin births. *Am. J. Hum. Genet., 34,* 988-998.

Windham, G. C., and Bjerkedal, T. (1984). Malformations in twins and their siblings, Norway, 1967-79. *Acta Genet. Med. Gemellol. (Roma), 33,* 87-95.

Woldringh, G. H., Besselink, D. E., Tillema, A. H., Hendriks, J. C., and Kremer, J. A. (2010). Karyotyping, birth defects and follow-up of children after intracytoplasmic sperm injection with non-ejaculated sperm: a systematic review. *Hum. Reprod. Update,* 16, 12-19.

Wright, V. C., Chang, J., Jeng, G., Macaluso, M.; Centers for Disease Control and Prevention (CDC). (2008). Assisted reproductive technology surveillance--United States, 2005. *MMWR. Surveill. Summ., 57,* 1-23.

Yan, J., Huang, G., Sun, Y., Zhao, X., Chen, S., Zou, S., et al. (2011). Birth defects after assisted reproductive technologies in China: analysis of 15,405 offspring in seven centers (2004 to 2008). *Fertil. Steril., 95,* 458-460.

Zhang, X. H., Qiu, L. Q., and Huang, J. P. (2011). Risk of birth defects increased in multiple births. *Birth Defects Res. A Clin. Mol. Teratol., 91,* 34-38.

Zimoń, T., Walczak, M., Fydryk, J., Materna-Kiryluk, A., Mejnartowicz, J., Latos-Bieleńska, A., et al. (1998). Prevalence and forms of congenital anomalies in twins born in Pomeranian District during the period from 1.07.1997 to 31.12.1998. Polish Register of Congenital Anomalies. *Acta Genet. Med. Gemellol. (Roma), 47,* 255-259.

In: Advances in Reproductive Technology ...   ISBN: 978-1-62417-875-7
Editor: Ignatz Sanger   © 2013 Nova Science Publishers, Inc.

Chapter 2

DOWN'S SYNDROME SCREENING IN ASSISTED CONCEPTION PREGNANCIES

Ido Ben-Ami and Ron Maymon[*]
Department of Obstetrics and Gynecology, Assaf Harofeh Medical Center,
Zerifin, Israel, affiliated with the Sackler School of Medicine,
Tel-Aviv University, Tel-Aviv, Israel

INTRODUCTION

Over the last three decades, prenatal screening for Down's syndrome (DS) has become an integrated part of antenatal care in most developed countries. In the second trimester, the most common markers are maternal serum human chorionic gonadotrophin (hCG) or its free β-subunit (Fβ-hCG), alpha-fetoprotein (AFP), and unconjugated estriol (uE$_3$). Large studies using combinations of hCG or Fβ-hCG and either or both of the other markers have confirmed model predictions that about two-thirds of DS-affected pregnancies can be detected with a false positive rate (FPR) of about 5% (Wald *et al.*, 1997; Cuckle, 1998a). The most recent addition to the second trimester serum markers has been Inhibin-A, which is found at higher levels in affected pregnancies (Van Lith *et al.*, 1992; Wald *et al.*, 1999a). This combination of markers (the "quadruple test") allows the detection of ~75% of DS-affected

[*] All correspondence: Ron Maymon, MD, Department of Obstetrics and Gynecology, Assaf Harofeh Medical Center, Zerifin, 70300, Israel. Telephone: +972-3-5245892, Fax: +972-3-5246867, E-mail: maymonrb@bezeqint.net.

pregnancies with a FPR of ~5% if gestational age is based on an ultrasound scan (Wald *et al.*, 2003a).

It is presently accepted that ultrasound can identify and measure subcutaneous fluid collections between the soft tissue covering the fetal spine and the overlying skin during the late first trimester (Szabo and Gellen, 1990; Pandya *et al.*, 1995a; Snijders *et al.*, 1998). The thickness of this hypoechoic ultrasonographic feature, defined as nuchal translucency (NT), is associated with chromosomal abnormalities (Szabo and Gellen, 1990; Pandya *et al.*, 1995; Snijders *et al.*, 1998), cardiac and other structural defects (Reynders *et al.*, 1997), as well as an increased risk of spontaneous abortion (Fukada *et al.*, 1997). In the first trimester, the combination of maternal serum pregnancy-associated placental protein-A (PAPP-A) and Fβ-hCG can achieve a detection rate of ~60% with a FPR of ~5% (Haddow *et al.*, 1998).

Combining NT with the above first trimester biochemical serum markers resulted in a combined screening test (Wald and Hackshaw, 1997). It has been reported that such a combination may allow about an 85% DS detection rate with a 5% FPR (De Biasio *et al.*, 1999; de Graaf *et al.*, 1999; Spencer *et al.*, 1999), a significant improvement of other DS screening tests. Later on, a model of an integrated screening for DS was proposed, which was based on combination of first trimester NT measurement and serum PAPP-A levels with second trimester AFP, β-hCG, E_3 and inhibin. The integrated test could allow a 90% DS detection rate for a 1% FPR (Wald *et al.*, 1999a).

Another sonographic marker which can be used both in the first and a second trimester in order to improve the prediction of DS is nasal bone (NB) evaluation. Cicero and colleagues (Cicero *et al.*, 2001) found that absence of the NB during first trimester sonography was associated with trisomy 21. The authors estimated that if NB assessment were combined with maternal age and NT measurement, 93% of DS cases would be detected at a 5% false-positive rate and that 85% of cases would still be detected if the false-positive rate were set at 1%. In subsequent studies, the same investigators found that an absent NB was also associated with trisomy 18, trisomy 13, and monosomy X (Cicero *et al.*, 2004). These data suggest that in high-risk pregnancies, NB assessment is a sensitive and highly specific marker and could be a useful adjunct to NT and serum biochemistry (Rosen *et al.*, 2007).

In addition to increased NT and absence NB, chromosomal abnormalities are associated with a pattern of characteristic sonographic findings in the first trimester. Trisomy 21 was found to be associated with reverse flow pattern in the ductus venosus, tricuspid regurgitation and maxillary hypoplasia (Borrell, 2009). Although first trimester sonographic markers are potentially the best, some concerns have arisen about their clinical application. Pitfalls may be due to inability to examine the markers, incorrect assessment, or incorrect interpretation of the findings (Borrell, 2009).

It is well known that the maternal serum concentrations of placental and fetal proteins may be affected by various conditions, such as diabetes mellitus, maternal smoking, multiple gestation, ethnic subgroups and wrong dates (Wald *et al.*, 1997). Therefore, adjustment criteria were introduced to correct the FPR and the detection rate (DR), thus providing a more accurate patient-specific calculated risk (Wald *et al.*, 1997).

Over the past decade, the wide use of various assisted reproduction technologies (ARTs) have risen dramatically. Women who conceived following ART have thus far received the same antenatal screening approach as those who conceived spontaneously (Maymon and Jauniaux, 2002). This policy would appear to be inadequate since women who conceived following ART treatment are generally older than are women with spontaneously conceived pregnancies, and are therefore at higher risk for a chromosomal disorder (primarily trisomy 21) (Geipel *et al.*, 1999; Pinborg *et al.*, 2004). Fetuses conceived after intracytoplasmic sperm injection (ICSI) are also known to have an increased risk of chromosomal aberrations (Aboulghar *et al.*, 2001; Bonduelle *et al.*, 2002; Gjerris *et al.*, 2008; Jozwiak *et al.*, 2004). In addition, these women may suffer from various underlying metabolic, endocrinological or genetic diseases, for which ART has been indicated in the first place (Maymon and Jauniaux, 2002). Taken together, these factors may lead to overuse of invasive cytogenetic testing and thus may contribute to the 20% amniocentesis rate in pregnant women who conceived with ART (Maymon *et al.*, 1999a). Besides the risk of miscarriage following an invasive procedure, 'high risk' results are associated with emotional sequelae as they raise the anxiety level throughout the process of counseling, invasive procedure and until a reassuring result is received.

The current chapter aims to explore the challenging issue of antenatal DS screening in pregnancies resulting from ART (high order multiple gestations, twins, and singletons). The implication and the management in the attempt to achieve the best evaluation of DS risk for every type of gestation will be discussed.

1. HIGH-ORDER MULTIPLE PREGNANCIES

The artificial production of large numbers of high order multiple gestations was followed by an urgent need to screen for DS among these pregnancies and the subsequent recognition of the complexity of such procedures.

Serum Screening

Triplet pregnancies are primarily iatrogenic conceptions following "successful" infertility therapy (Berkowitz *et al.*, 1996). In such a selected population, serum screening is not widely applicable, although studies have been published (Spencer *et al.*, 1994). Furthermore, the use of fetal reduction, which parallels the widespread use of assisted conception (Maymon *et al.*, 1995; Berkowitz *et al.*, 1996), further complicates the screening algorithm, mainly because elevated mid gestation maternal serum AFP levels are present after first trimester fetal reduction. Grau and co-workers (Grau *et al.*, 1990) reviewed maternal serum and amniotic fluid levels of AFP from 40 women who underwent fetal reduction at approximately 12 weeks of gestation. Respectively, 95% and 25% of the patients who had mid gestation AFP measured in maternal serum and amniotic fluid had elevated values. Fortunately, none of those abnormal levels were associated with neural tube defects, although two structural defects were detected by other means. The difference between serum and amniotic fluid AFP was attributed to either one or several mechanisms: All pregnancies were reduced to twins, and one to triplets and it is not uncommon to find elevated maternal serum AFP in such pregnancies. Alternatively, fetal AFP could have been released from the dead fetuses because of their having undergone autholysis (Lynch and Berkowitz, 1993). In such circumstances, the transport of AFP across fetal membranes and the placenta may be enhanced by the remaining live co-twin(s) (Grau *et al.*, 1990). Lynch and Berkowitz (1993) reported similar findings and concluded that mid gestation maternal serum AFP is always elevated after multifetal pregnancy reduction and thus is not necessarily indicative of fetal defects. In contrast, Groutz *et al.* (1996) found elevated AFP maternal serum in only two of the 28 studied cases, both having adverse perinatal outcomes; i.e. severe pre-eclampsia in one, and exomphalos in the other.

Several groups (Groutz *et al.*, 1996; Shulman *et al.*, 1996; Shulman and Phillips, 1997) studied the effect of first trimester fetal reduction on the triple test results (AFP; uE_3 and hCG), and confirmed the elevation of maternal serum AFP. Rotmensch *et al.* (1999) reported mid gestation triple serum screening results from 27 high-order multiple gestations reduced to twins. About 90% of women exhibited maternal serum AFP levels >2 MoM, but only one of the newborns had structural anomalies. In their experience, this marker didn't correlate with either the number of reduced fetuses or with adverse obstetric outcome. In this study, however, the mean hCG and uE_3 serum levels were slightly increased as well (1.22±0.49 MoM; 1.15±0.31 MoM, respectively). Although previous studies found that both hCG and E_3 were not altered (Shulman *et al.*, 1996; Shulman and Phillips, 1997), the effect of first trimester reduction on DS screening efficacy remains undetermined (Groutz *et al.*, 1996; Shulman *et al.*, 1996; Shulman and Phillips, 1997; Rotmensch *et al.*, 1999), and amniocentesis is not indicated in those cases. Moreover, ultrasonography for evaluation of fetal anatomy should be considered mainly because maternal serum AFP cannot be used in these patients to screen for fetal abnormalities (Lynch and Berkowitz, 1993). Finally, it was found that following multifetal reduction to twin pregnancies, the maternal serum levels of inhibin A decrease to the level of twin pregnancies during the second trimester. It was concluded that inhibin A may be effectively used as a marker for DS screening in cases of twin pregnancy following multifetal reduction (Chen *et al.*, 2007).

Ultrasound Screening

Because NT is perceived as a valuable marker for detecting fetal abnormalities and complications, its importance is clear-cut for multiple pregnancies in which biochemical screening is of limited value. In twin pregnancies, first trimester NT screening for chromosomal abnormalities was found both reliable and feasible (Pandya *et al.*, 1995b). Our group assessed pregnant patients who conceived following assisted reproduction and were carrying ≥3 fetuses (Maymon *et al.*, 1999b). Each fetus was ultrasonographically assessed by measuring the CRL and NT thickness using a published protocol (Pandya *et al.*, 1995a; Snijders *et al.*, 1998).

Twenty-four pregnant patients, initially carrying 79 fetuses aged between 10-14 weeks of gestation, were compared with consecutively matched singleton controls (Maymon *et al.*, 1999b). NT measurements were feasible for both study and control fetuses, which exhibited similar NT measurements for the 5th, 50th and 95th centiles. Also, mean NT thicknesses (mm or MOMs) were similar for both groups (1.41 ± 0.41 mm and 1.35 ± 0.39 mm, respectively and 0.87 ± 0.23 MOM and 0.83 ± 0.25 MOM, respectively). Moreover, contrary to others who have reported obtaining an NT thickness only in about 83% of the assessed singletons (Haddow *et al.*, 1998), we succeeded in measuring it in all of our cases (Maymon *et al.*, 1999b). No instances of chromosomal abnormalities were detected in either group, and of those infants who had no karyotyping, no traits were observed postnatally that warranted a chromosomal analysis. As there is no other effective screening modality for these pregnancies, it is reasonable to recommend NT measurement for antenatal screening services for higher order multiple gestations (Maymon *et al.*, 1999b; Maymon and Jauniaux, 2002; Ben-Ami and Maymon, 2012). Similar results with our experience were found by Maslovitz *et al.* (2004) who reported their experience on NT measurement among 3128 and 51 singletons and triplets pregnancies, respectively. Accordingly, the mean nuchal translucency thickness was 1.23 mm for singletons and triplets. The 5th and 95th percentiles were also the same between the 2 studied groups. The regression curves of 5th, 50th, and 95th percentiles of NT plotted against crown-rump length (CRL) of triplets and singletons overlapped. Based on the above, the authors have concluded that NT values and distribution are the same in triplets and singletons, validating the utility of the cutoff values.

In order to enhance the method for calculating fetus-specific DS risk in triplets, the between-fetus correlation coefficient of log NT, in multiples of the median, was estimated from a series of 95 unaffected triplets (Cuckle *et al.*, 2012). A trivariate log Gaussian model was used to calculate likelihood ratios for discordant and concordant Down's syndrome. Applying these to the prior maternal age-specific risk yielded risks in monozygous, dizygous and trizygous twins. The weighted average risk was then computed with weights relating to chorionicity and assisted reproduction.

Accordingly, it was found that the correlation coefficient in unaffected pregnancies was 0.408 ($P<0.0001$; 95% confidence interval 0.30-0.50) and estimated to be 0.205 and 0.107 in triplets pairs with one or two affected fetuses. The illustration showed very large differences could be obtained in the risks when the extent of correlation in NT between fetuses is taken into account and when the measurements are treated as independent. Based on the above, it has been concluded that fetus-specific DS risks in triplets should be calculated using its own NT value as well as that in the other fetuses (Cuckle *et al.*, 2012).

We believe our observations (Maymon *et al.*, 1999b) validate the using of NT measurements originally obtained in singletons (Pandya *et al.*, 1995a;

Snijders *et al.*, 1998) and twins (Pandya *et al.*, 1995b; Sebire *et al.*, 1996, 2000) among higher-order multiple gestations. More studies are needed for different types of multiple pregnancies to verify the assumptions we and others have made. Meanwhile, the strong correlations in NT measurements between triplet fetuses cannot be ignored and the estimation of DS risk in a given fetus is determined by NT values in three fetuses (Cuckle *et al.*, 2012).

Screening before Multifetal Pregnancy Reduction

A critical problem of high-order multiple gestation management protocols is fetal reduction. Most authorities agree that reducing multifetal pregnancies to twins improves pregnancy and perinatal outcome (Berkowitz *et al.*, 1996). Furthermore, this sonographic screening method provides additional data for the identification of an abnormal fetus, thus lowering the complications of leaving an abnormal one after the reduction (Berkowitz *et al.*, 1993). In addition, this possibility offers an alternative, aside from terminating the entire pregnancy, to those women carrying either a higher number of fetuses than desired (Maymon *et al.*, 1995).

Fetal reduction is commonly carried out at the end of the first trimester through a transabdominal intrathoracic introduction of a fine needle under ultrasound guidance and injection of concentrated potassium chloride solution (Maymon *et al.*, 1995; Berkowitz *et al.*, 1993). Whilst agreement exists (Maymon *et al.*, 1995; Berkowitz *et al.*, 1993) as to the number of fetuses to be left (twin pregnancies having the best outcome) (Evans *et al.*, 2001), the choice as to which fetuses to terminate is governed by a number of variables. Thus, before feticide, a careful ultrasonographic assessment of the entire pregnancy is recommended to determine the actual number of living fetuses, their location, the placentation for monochorionic twins (Sepulveda *et al.*, 1996), presence of visible fetal anomalies, or fetal discordancy (Dickey *et al.*, 1992; Maymon *et al.*, 1995), as well as slower fetal heart rate (Achiron *et al.*, 1991). Those parameters may indicate an anomaly or poor prognosis for the survival of that fetus (Achiron *et al.*, 1991; Dickey *et al.*, 1992). Additionally, it seems important to offer pre-procedure, noninvasive genetic testing and a careful scanning, especially for those patients with a significantly increased risk of karyotypic abnormalities by virtue of their age (Berkowitz *et al.*, 1993).

Berkowitz *et al.* (1993) have reported that among 200 patients who underwent fetal reduction, 6 of the remaining fetuses had either anatomic (Snijders *et al.*, 1998) or chromosomal (Haddow *et al.*, 1998) abnormalities.

Based on this observation, pre-procedure genetic counseling and careful scanning was proposed, especially for those patients with an increased risk of karyotype abnormalities (Berkowitz *et al.*, 1993). To overcome such problems, first trimester ultrasound screening using NT measurements seems to be a most promising option.

Lipitz *et al.* (2001) recommend performance of fetal reduction in triplets at 13-14 weeks' gestation rather than 11-12 weeks; as this allows a more detailed anomaly scan at a slightly more advanced gestational age. According to their experience, pregnancy loss was similar (about 4%) in either group. They concluded that screening before fetal reduction at 13-14 weeks' should include NT measurement and ruling out relative intrauterine growth restriction and structural anomalies. At this gestational age, the sex of the fetus can also be determined, a factor which may be of clinical importance for families at risk for chromosomal X-linked disorders. In triplet pregnancies, such an early detailed fetal anomaly scan requires a very experienced sonographer and a modern ultrasound machine with high resolution.

Since the transvaginal sonography provides a better image of the lower fetus, combined transvaginal and transabdominal scan may be required (Cicero *et al.*, 2001). With such high scanning performance, it seems reasonable to consider additional sonographic markers or fetal biometric measurements such as the fetal NB, flow velocity patterns in the ductus venosus, tricuspid regurgitation and maxillary hypoplasia at the time of an NT scan (Cuckle, 2002). Several studies have recently incorporated NB measurement (Zoppi *et al.*, 2003; Sepulveda *et al.*, 2009) and even first trimester biochemistry (Krantz *et al.*, 2011) in the DS screening test in triplets. However, NB assessment is not only limited in sensitivity but also more challenging in multiple than in singleton pregnancies owing to difficulties in obtaining adequate views of the fetal face (Sepulveda *et al.*, 2009). Additional studies are needed to determine the most efficient screening combination by means of ultrasound for the subgroup of high order multiple gestation.

There is overlap between the optimal gestational ages for multi-fetal pregnancy reduction and NT screening. Therefore, in recent years some groups (Maymon *et al.*, 1999b; Monni *et al.*, 1999; Maslovitz *et al.*, 2004) have routinely used NT measurement to select for reduction the fetus with the highest aneuploidy risk. Our algorithm for risk calculation in twins (Cuckle and Maymon, 2010) and the current algorithm (Cuckle *et al.*, 2012) for triplets will improve the accuracy of this selection.

Brambati and colleagues (1995) and Eddleman and coworkers (2000) reported performing chorionic villous sampling (CVS) before multifetal pregnancy reduction. The message from these two studies is that in high-risk groups for chromosomal aneuploidy, CVS should be offered before embryo reduction is employed. Eddleman *et al.* (2000) further supported their management protocol by stating that "rarely, there is a visible anomaly or a smaller than expected CRL that influences the decision about which fetus to remove". According to their report, however, CVS procedures alone were associated with 1.2% sampling errors, which is actually the primary risk for aneuploidy in this group.

Although pre-reduction CVS has its advantages, primarily in older patients, the following disadvantages hinder the widespread use of this practice: the risk of abortion; the objective difficulty in carrying out villocentesis in multiple pregnancies; the difficulty in identifying ill fetuses to be eliminated within a few days of taking the sample; and the higher stress level in patients caused by the two invasive procedures carried out within a few days of each other (Maymon and Herman, 2001).

It is our contention to suggest the following approach, which includes NT measurement as part of pre-procedure noninvasive genetic testing, before any embryo reduction. This is followed by the reducing the one exhibiting the highest risk, once such a fetus is detected and thereby lowering the probability of leaving an affected fetus after the procedure (Berkowitz *et al.*, 1993). Using this policy we encountered a triplet pregnancy in which one fetus exhibited a NT of 3 mm (>95th centile for CRL (Maymon and Herman, 2001)). The other two fetuses had NT within the normal limit for gestation (Maymon and Herman, 2001). Before reducing that fetus and by using the same fine needle, a few milliliters of amniotic fluid were aspirated for chromosomal analysis. This test revealed a fetus affected with trisomy 13. Mid gestation amniocentesis performed later confirmed euploid karyotype of the remaining fetuses. Similar experience was reported by Monni *et al.* (1999).

Our current policy (Maymon *et al.*, 1999b; Maymon and Herman, 2001; Ben-Ami and Maymon, 2012; see Figure 1) is:

1. Routine examination of fetal NT and determination of chorionicity before any multifetal pregnancy reduction. Examination of NB, flow velocity patterns in the ductus venosus, tricuspid regurgitation and maxillary hypoplasia is reserved for high risk cases. Patients could be offered to postpone the reduction around 14 weeks after detailed anomaly scan.

2. Reduction and karyotyping of the high risk one and or the malformed one.
3. Performance of mid gestation amniocentesis, where indicated.

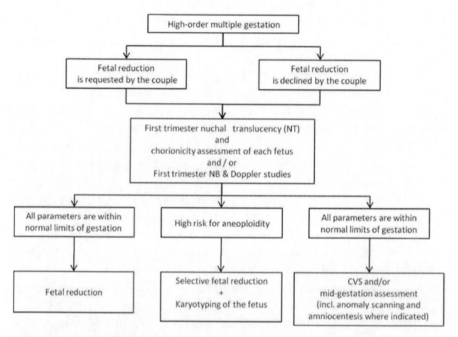

Figure 1. Flow chart of first-trimester screening for chromosomal abnormalities in high-order multiple gestation (modified from Ben-Ami and Maymon, 2012). Fetal reduction could be postponed until after detailed anomaly scan (around 13-14 weeks' gestation). Chorionic villous sampling (CVS) is reserved for only high-risk cases for chromosomal aberrations or carriers of a single gene disorder or balanced translocation.
NB=nasal bone.

The performance of genetic amniocentesis after multifetal pregnancy reduction doesn't increase the risk of pregnancy loss over that observed in association with reduction itself (Selam *et al.*, 1999). We think that CVS should be reserved only to highly selected instance, including parents with balance translocations or carriers of a single gene disorder in which prenatal diagnosis is available.

Conclusion

Women who conceive multifetal pregnancy after assisted conception are naturally wary of any invasive prenatal diagnostic procedure. As they receive careful antenatal care from the start of their pregnancies, and because their serum markers are less discriminative for chromosomal screening, it seems reasonable to offer them ultrasound assessment including NT measurement, which presently is the only available and highly efficient screening method. This valuable information can contribute to overall management if fetal reduction is planned and as a screening modality for other structural anomalies associated with increased NT.

2. TWIN PREGNANCIES

Twin pregnancies are becoming more frequent in most developed countries due to the increased use of ART and advanced maternal age. The combined effect results in older women having a greater chance of conceiving twins (Spencer, 2000). These pregnancies present numerous diagnostic and management challenges from conception to delivery. They may be at a higher risk for chromosomal abnormality (Cuckle, 1998b) as well as for structural defects (Doyle et al., 1991). The methods widely used for DS screening in twins include maternal age, midgestation maternal serum screening and first-trimester NT measurements (with or without serum markers). Screening of twin pregnancies is considered to be extremely difficult because of the clinical, technical and ethical challenges posed for diagnosis and clinical management of such pregnancies (Cuckle, 1998b; Spencer and Nicolaides, 2003) with some centers not offering DS screening in twin pregnancies (Wenstrom et al., 1993; Shetty and Smith, 2005).

Second Trimester Screening

Since serum screening was introduced before the other methods, there is more experience with it worldwide. It is now accepted, however, that DS serum screening is of limited value in twin pregnancies (Wald et al., 1991; Cuckle, 1998b). For example, modeling predicts that in 30-year-old women, second-trimester AFP, uE3, Fβ-hCG and inhibin with a 1 in 250 term cut-off risk will detect just one-quarter of affected twin pregnancies compared with two-thirds in singletons, albeit with fewer false positives. The reason for the poorer results is that in twins that are discordant for DS, feto-placental products from the unaffected fetus can mask the abnormal levels produced by the affected fetus (Cuckle, 1998b). Furthermore, whilst a pregnancy at high risk may be identified, serum biochemistry results will not be able to pinpoint which twin is affected (Spencer and Nicolaides, 2003).

It is well established that all the serum markers used in DS screening are increased about two-fold, on average, in twins. The interpretation of screening tests in twins is similar to singletons, in that a DS risk is estimated from the maternal age and overlapping marker distributions. For DS twin pregnancies, the average level although increased is not doubled and can be calculated from the averages in DS and unaffected singletons (Cuckle, 1998b). Despite these limitations, some centers still offer mid-gestation serum screening for twin pregnancies, either because of a limited capacity for first trimester screening or due to women booking late for prenatal care.

Two studies that compared DS screening tests in unaffected IVF and spontaneous twin pregnancies used this screening method (Raty *et al.*, 2000; Maymon *et al.*, 2005). In the former, the authors showed Fβ-hCG levels to be 20% higher in IVF twin pregnancies compared to spontaneously-conceived ones (2.20 MoM versus 1.83 MoM, respectively). This difference was of only marginal statistical significance ($P = 0.08$). No difference was observed in AFP MoM levels between the two twin groups. The authors concluded that because of the increased false positive rate (FPR) in this population, these issues should be discussed when offering mid-gestation DS screening test in IVF twin pregnancies (Raty *et al.*, 2000). In the second study, there was no significant difference in the mean MoM value of the triple serum analytes, although the ART cases had the highest hCG levels (Maymon *et al.*, 2005). Possible reasons for the higher hCG levels may be either the medication associated with ART, advanced maternal age, or placentation failure in IVF gestation (Raty *et al.*, 2000).

There is only limited data regarding serum inhibin levels in ART pregnancies. Our group (Maymon *et al.*, 2006) found that there was not statistically significant difference between the median serum inhibin levels of 37 ART twin pregnancies and 50 spontaneous twin pregnancies (1.98 and 2.18 MoM, respectively, $P = 0.62$).

First Trimester Screening

A cornerstone in first-trimester evaluation in twins is an accurate determination of the chorionicity (Sepulveda, 1997). Ultrasound, using single or composite parameters, has enabled the determination of chorionicity in the majority of cases. Determination of chorionicity becomes increasingly difficult with advancing gestational age and high-resolution first-trimester or early second-trimester (10–14 weeks) abdominal or transvaginal sonography has been shown to offer the highest specificity and sensitivity in diagnosing chorionicity (Shetty and Smith, 2005).

The 'lambda' sign (also known as 'twin peak' sign) is referred to the triangular projection of tissue extending up to the base of the inter-twin membrane in dichorionic placentation. This term represents the echodense chorionic villi between the two layers of chorion at its origin from the placenta. As the pregnancy advances into the second and third trimesters, regression of the chorion frondosum to form chorion laeve means that the twin peak sign cannot be reliably used to determine chorionicity. Traditionally, the membrane 'take-off' in a monochorionic gestation has been described with the 'T' sign, where the membrane approaches the placenta at around a 90° angle (Shetty and Smith, 2005).

Although one may expect that the majority of ART twins are dichorionic, an increased incidence of monozygotic twining is reported in these pregnancies (Wenstrom et al., 1993). One theory behind this observation is minor trauma to the blastocyst during the process of ART (Wenstrom et al., 1993). Early detection of monochorionic twins has major implications for pregnancy management especially if invasive karyotyping or selective fetal reduction is later indicated.

In twin pregnancies discordant for DS maternal serum markers have much poorer discriminatory power than in singletons (Cuckle and Benn, 2010) which is not the case for NT and other ultrasound markers. Consequently, although the combined test has a slightly higher detection rate than NT screening, many practitioners prefer the latter when calculating the fetus-specific risk for DS. Indeed, in a study of 60 unaffected twins that sequentially underwent both first-trimester NT and mid-gestation triple serum screening, the screen-positive rate was found to be much lower using NT measurements alone than mid-gestation serum (5% versus 15%). Thus, in twins, serum screening may lead to an 18% amniocentesis rate in this group (Maymon et al., 1999c). This has serious perinatal consequences since the fetal loss related to amniocentesis is more than double in twins compared to matched singletons (Kidd et al.,

1997). Since NT screening is fetus specific, it is regarded as the method of choice both for spontaneous and ART twin pregnancies (Maymon and Jauniaux, 2002; see Figure 2). This is supported by the observation that NT in DS fetuses was found to be similar to that found in affected singletons (Pandya *et al.*, 1995a).

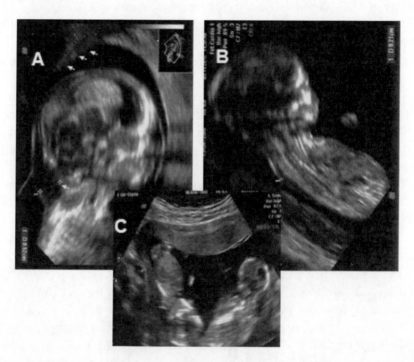

Figure 2: Montage plate of a 12 weeks dichorionic ART twin pregnancy discordant for their nuchal translucency thickness. A. Mid-sagittal view of the affected co-twin showing the increased (5.2 mm) nuchal translucency (arrow head) and the twin peak sign of the dichorionic twins (arrows). B. Mid-sagittal view of the unaffected co-twin. Note the thin (2.1 mm) nuchal translucency. C. Longitudinal view of both twins.

The common fetus-specific method of calculating DS risk in twins assumes that the NT measurements in the two fetuses are independent and this is now known to be incorrect. In a series of 181 unaffected twins from Denmark (Wøjdemann *et al.*, 2006) reported a correlation coefficient of 0.34 between the pairs of NTs, expressed in log MoMs for CRL. A similar substantial degree of correlation was found both in the 31 monochorionic, with a correlation coefficient of 0.40, and in the 150 dichorionic twins, with a correlation coefficient of 0.32 (Wøjdemann *et al.*, 2006). Similarly, recent study reported a correlation coefficient of 0.43 in 246 dichorionic twins with euploid fetuses (Cuckle and Maymon, 2010).

Thus, with NT screening, each fetus is considered like a singleton and a fetus-specific risk is calculated from the NT and CRL. However, the NT measurements is dependent on both the specific NT and that of its co-twin, with reported correlation coefficients in two series of 0.34 (Wøjdemann et al., 2006) and 0.45 (Cuckle and Maymon, 2010) between log multiples of the median (MoM) for CRL. An algorithm has been published to calculate these dependent risks (Cuckle and Maymon, 2010). At 12 weeks of gestation, the model predicted detection rate for a 3% FPR was 68% when between-fetus correlation is not taken into account, increasing to 73% when this model was applied (Cuckle and Maymon, 2010). Similarly, for other false-positive rates and gestational weeks there was a predicted 4-6% increase in detection (Cuckle and Maymon, 2010). We conclude that using a fetus-specific DS risk algorithm leads to a worthwhile increase in detection (Maymon et al., 2011).

In multiple pregnancies, the maternal age-specific DS risks, meaning that at least one fetus is affected, is no higher in twins than in singletons (Cuckle, 1998b). Caution is needed when interpreting the maternal age background risk in cases of oocyte donation. In this case, the age of the donor should be used for the DS risk calculation. Within this context, it is vital to define a prior risk for each fetus, which is half the age-specific risk as that in a singleton (Wald et al., 2003b).

Excluding one report, which demonstrated a significantly lower NT (0.88 MoM) in IVF twins (Orlandi et al., 2002), most studies found no difference in the NT measurements median (mm) and mean (MoM) NT among ART twins compared to spontaneous twins ((Maymon et al., 1999a; Maymon et al., 2001). The IVF group had a lower FPR by a combination of first-trimester NT and maternal age (6.5% compared to 10 and 13% for the controlled ovarian hyperstimulation and spontaneous twins respectively), but this value did not reach a level of statistical significance.

In singleton pregnancies, it is possible to use additional ultrasound markers determined at the same time as NT measurement, to modify the estimated DS risk. The most widely used are absence of the fetal NB, pulse-wave Doppler to determine abnormal blood flow in the ductus venosus and tricuspid regurgitation. Of these markers the only information on inter-fetal concordance in multiple pregnancies is for ductus venosus A-wave reversal in twins (Maiz et al., 2009). Among 516 dichorionic twins, there was no concordance since 43 (8.3%) had reversal in at least one fetus and 4 of the 43 (9.3%) had reversal in both. However, among 179 monochorionic twins there was concordance: 33 (18%) had reversal and in 12 of the 33 (36%) it was reversed in both.

There are only limited data available on the use of NB evaluation for DS risk assessment in multiple gestations. In a retrospective study it was shown that the addition of NB to NT, PAPP-A, and Fβ-hCG increased the DS DR from 79 to 89% at a 5% FPR. It was concluded that in twins, first-trimester screening with NB is valuable (Cleary-Goldman *et al.*, 2008). Sepulveda *et al.* (2009) and Zoppi *et al.* (2003) have included NB measurement to NT assessment in twin pregnancies.

According to their experience, NB measurement is feasible also in those pregnancies. However this is a very difficult measurement, owing to the limitation in obtaining adequate views of the fetal face in multiple pregnancies (Sepulveda *et al.*, 2009)

Combined NT and Serum Markers

As in singleton pregnancies, combining the NT results with the serum markers in twin pregnancies is likely to yield a better screening performance than that obtained using either NT or serum markers alone (Wenstrom *et al.*, 1993; Maymon *et al.*, 2005). However, in twin pregnancies, interpreting all the results of these markers is more difficult because the serum biochemistry concentration relates to the pregnancy while each NT measurement is fetus specific. Therefore, combination of serum and NT measurements results in the calculation of a pregnancy-specific estimation.

Assuming that first- and second-trimester serum analytes are not correlated and that the levels of serum markers are twice that expected in singletons (Spencer *et al.*, 1994; Wald *et al.*, 1997; Cuckle, 1998b), the models of combining the likelihood ratio (LR) of NT in MOMs and serum biochemistry of each co-twin can be applied as they are in singletons. The larger of the two CRLs should be used to estimate the overall gestational age for use in determining the MoMs. The overall DS risk can be calculated from the sum of the two individual nuchal translucency LR's multiplied by the biochemistry LR (Maymon *et al.*, 2005).

Lately, studies have been focused on possible differences in biochemical markers distribution between monochorionic and dichorionic twins (Linskens *et al.*, 2009; Koster *et al.*, 2010; Madsen *et al.*, 2011). Spencer (2001) showed that there was no statistical difference between the markers' distribution among unaffected monochorionic and dichorionic twins. Gonce *et al.* (2005)

demonstrated that weight-corrected MoM free-β-hCG are significantly reduced in monochorionic compared with dichorionic twins in samples taken before 12weeks' gestation. Following a wider study, Spencer *et al.* (2008) concluded that there were statistical differences in PAPP-A levels, but not the values of free-β-hCG. More recently, Linskens *et al.* (2009 concluded that there were statistical differences in PAPP-A levels and in the values of free-β-hCG, as well. However, Koster *et al.* (2010) concluded there were no significant differences in biochemical parameters despite chorionicity. Madsen *et al.* (2011) demonstrated that medians for the two biochemical markers for monochorionic and dichorionic twins in unaffected pregnancies show a gestational age-specific increase relative to singleton medians highlighting the importance of generation chorionicity-specific medians for these markers in twins. Finally, Prats *et al.* (2012) examined the distribution of first-trimester biochemical markers of aneuploidy in twins according to chorionicity. Free-β-hCG and PAPP-A distributions were significantly lower in monochorionic than in dichorionic twins.

In a study which examined the effect of IVF on first-trimester serum markers and NT in 30 twins (16 IVF and 14 ICSI), no difference was found in the levels of Fβ-hCG, PAPP-A between the study cases and the control cases (Orlandi *et al.*, 2002). Another group has suggested combining the individual fetal NT with the results of serum markers, thereby obtaining the entire pregnancy-specific 'pseudorisk' (Wald *et al.*, 2003b). According to this model, for a 5% FPR NT alone, first-trimester combined NT and serum biochemistry as well as the integrated tests will yield 69%, 72% and 80% detection rate, respectively. Similar first-trimester screening results were also reported by another group (Spencer, 2000). However, in contrast to second-trimester screening, chorionicity had no impact on the first-trimester serum biochemical marker levels in twin pregnancies (Spencer, 2001). In a later study, Spencer and Nicolaides (2003) reported their experience for DS screening in the first trimester of 230 twin pregnancies (21% conceived by ART) using the combination of maternal serum biochemistry and NT: 9.2% of these pregnancies were found to be screen positive similar to our current NT screening results. Therefore, adding first-trimester maternal serum biochemistry to NT may improve the detection rate by about 5–6%. However, when invasive testing is indicated, NT alone is the screening modality women should be counseled to choose, since ultrasound is the best means of specifically locating the affected co-twin (Spencer and Nicolaides, 2003).

To the best of our knowledge only one study (Raty *et al.*, 2000) has reported mid-gestation Fβ-hCG levels to be 20% higher in IVF twin pregnancies compared to spontaneously conceived ones. This difference was of only marginal statistical significance. Another small series found high levels of hCG and uE3 among ART twins, which was not statistically significant (Maymon *et al.*, 2005).

The vanishing twin (VT) phenomenon is the disappearance of an entire gestational sac or one of the fetuses after documented fetal heart activity in multiple pregnancies (Jauniaux *et al.*, 1988). The increasing use of high-resolution ultrasound in early pregnancy has demonstrated that this phenomenon, is a rather a frequent incident (20–40%) (Landy and Keith, 1998; Dickey *et al.*, 2002). A VT is likely to have similar aetiology i.e. mainly the association with a chromosomal abnormality (Greenwold and Jauniaux, 2002). This could explain why the rate of VT after IVF-ICSI is lower at around 9% as the IVF procedure of embryo selection decreases the risk of transferring morphologically abnormal conceptions (Jauniaux *et al.*, 2010). Early implantation crowding, resulting in an unfavourable placentation of one of the gestational sac, or the consequence of major intrauterine bleeding with the formation of a large hematoma involving the definitive placenta of one of the gestational sacs have also been proposed as possible etiologies for a VT (Jauniaux *et al.*, 2010; Barton *et al.*, 2011).

In case of VT after ART, MS hCG exhibits a slower rise from Day 12 of pregnancy when compared with normally progressing twin pregnancies. From Day 44, the rate of serum hCG increment is similar, but with absolute hCG concentrations of less than half in VT pregnancies compared with normally progressing twin pregnancies (Kelly *et al.*, 1991). Gjerris *et al.* (2009a) have reported that women with ART pregnancies, who are diagnosed with a VT at 8–9 weeks, can have the 11-14 weeks combined screening for DS using the same risk calculation algorithm as in singleton ART pregnancies. In cases of VT diagnosed later in pregnancy, i.e. at the time of the NT scan, it is uncertain whether the serum risk assessment is as precise as in singleton ART pregnancies. In a recent review, Gjerris *et al.* (2012) have concluded that first trimester screening after VT should be based solely on the maternal age and the NT scan as biomarkers are significantly altered in these cases. In cases of VT, we suggest that the risk assessment should be based on ultrasonographic markers alone, including NT as all these markers are unaffected by the initial number of fetuses, number of placentas and chorionicity.

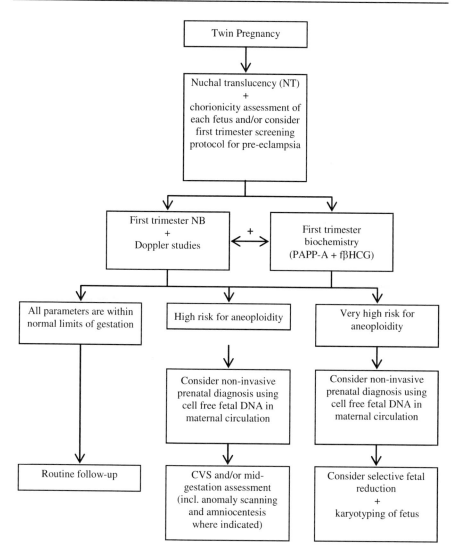

Figure 3. Flow chart of first-trimester screening for chromosomal abnormalities in twin pregnancy (modified from Ben-Ami and Maymon, 2012). Selective fetal reduction could be postponed until after detailed anomaly scan (around 13-14 weeks' gestation). Chorionic villous sampling (CVS) is reserved for high-risk cases for chromosomal aberrations or carriers of a single gene disorder or balanced translocation.
NB=nasal bone; PAPP-A= pregnancy-associated placental protein-A; fβ-hCG=free β-subunit of human chorionic gonadotrophin.

Conclusion

Mid-gestation serum screening alone is of limited value in ART-achieved twin pregnancies, and in view of the impressive progress recently achieved using early ultrasound it should be abandoned. The benefits of an algorithm that combines NT and serum biochemistry are that it may increase the detection rates to the level of singletons, and may even reduce the FPR. Since those women receive careful prenatal care from early in their pregnancies, it seems reasonable to offer them ultrasound screening by NT measurement. Presently, it is the best available modality and a highly efficient screening method for multiple pregnancies. The valuable information obtained early in gestation including chorionicity determination can contribute to overall management if either fetal reduction is planned or as a screening modality for other structural anomalies associated with increased NT (see Figure 3).

3. SINGLETON PREGNANCIES

In ART pregnancies the gestational age can be calculated from the oocyte retrieval, nevertheless an 'artificial menstrual dating' is constructed by calculating the oocyte retrieval minus two weeks or embryo-transfer minus 16 days to convert the menstrual dating. This date is then considered the basis for further gestational age calculation.

Second Trimester Screening

Chronologically, second trimester serum screening was introduced first and thus more experience has been gained with it. There is conflicting data in the literature surrounding maternal serum triple marker screening analyte levels and the DS FPR in pregnancies conceived through ART (Table 1). Several studies have found insignificant changes in maternal serum hCG concentrations in pregnancies achieved by ART treatment compared with naturally conceived pregnancies. Other authors, however, have found higher hCG concentrations in pregnancies resulting from ART compared with spontaneous pregnancies (overall range: 0.88-1.53 multiples of the mean (MoM), Table 1) (Barkai *et al.*, 1996; Heinonen *et al.*, 1996; Ribbert *et al.*, 1996; Frishman *et al.*, 1997; Wald *et al.*, 1999b; Bar-Hava *et al.*, 2001;

Maymon and Shulman, 2001, 2002; Perheentupa *et al.*, 2002; Raty *et al.*, 2002; Muller *et al.*, 2003; Rice *et al.*, 2005).

High hCG levels may be explained partly by a greater number of corpora lutea (Frishman *et al.*, 1997), by undiagnosed multiple early implantation sites or by progesterone supplementation, which increases placental hCG production (Weisz and Rodeck, 2006). Nevertheless, it is unlikely that most of these proteins will remain in the maternal circulation for as long as 4 months when the biochemical screening is performed (Marrs *et al.*, 1979; Ribbert *et al.*, 1996). Alternatively, it may represent placentation failure that could result in changes in the trophoblast function and thus hCG production (Maymon *et al.*, 1999b).

Women who conceived after oocyte donation represent a unique clinical model, since these women lack a corpus luteum and no induction of ovulation could have been carried out (Maymon and Shulman, 2001,2002; Shulman and Maymon, 2003). Unlike what occurs in self-oocytes IVF, where multiple corpora lutea may produce very high concentrations of progesterone, in oocyte donation pregnancies the progesterone is exclusively derived from therapeutic source. Hence, the changes in the second trimester serum markers can be attributed almost entirely to changes in the feto-placental unit metabolism. A comparison of maternal serum screening results between 37 oocyte donation and 46 self-oocytes IVF-conceived singletons of similarly aged women revealed a similar daily pattern of first trimester serum β-hCG in both groups. Importantly, these maternal serum hCG concentrations were found to be higher when compared to spontaneous pregnancies from the same population (1.38 and 1.32 median MoM for IVF and oocyte donation respectively, in comparison with 0.99 median MoM from the same reference laboratory; Maymon and Shulman, 2001; Table 1). Since neither chromosomal abnormalities nor fetal or neonatal deaths were recorded in either group, it was concluded that the high maternal serum hCG concentrations may be a marker for other adverse obstetric outcome rather than indicating a higher risk for a DS fetus (Maymon and Shulman, 2001).

The effect of ART on AFP and uE3 levels is also controversial (Table 1). Several studies have demonstrated decreased levels of maternal serum AFP and uE3 in IVF-conceived pregnancies (Ribbert *et al.*, 1996; Frishman *et al.*, 1997; Wald *et al.*, 1999b; Lam *et al.*, 1999; Muller *et al.*, 2003), while others found insignificant changes in their concentrations compared with naturally conceived pregnancies (Heinonen *et al.*, 1996; Bar-Hava *et al.*, 2001; Rice *et al.*, 2005). Interestingly, pregnancies resulting from oocyte donation showed 45% increase in AFP concentrations, which could not be explained by the age-related 4.4% per 10-year increment of serum AFP concentrations (Maymon and Shulman, 2001). Likewise, the median levels of both AFP and uE3 were found to be significantly higher in women using a donor oocyte versus those using their own oocytes, although it was concluded that these changes are not large enough to warrant correction of AFP and uE3. A comparison between two groups of unstimulated assisted-conception pregnancies, that is, own-oocyte frozen embryos (own-FET) versus oocyte-donated embryos, revealed that the oocyte-donated group had only significantly increased AFP concentrations compared to the own-FET group (1.38 versus 0.99 median MoM respectively, P = 0.002) (Shulman and Maymon, 2003). In contrast, pregnancies conceived by intrauterine insemination often present with lower maternal serum AFP than naturally conceived pregnancies (Hsu et al., 1999).

Table 1. The biochemistry serum screening profile in pregnancies achieved by ART

Assisted mode of conception	No. of cases	AFP MoM	uE3 MoM	hCG MoM	Reference
IVF	67	0.89	NR	1.23	Ribbert et al., 1996
IVF	41	1.02	NR	1.52	Heinonen et al., 1996
IVF	327	0.98	0.92	0.93	Barkai et al., 1996
IVF	69	0.95	0.9	1.22	Frishman et al., 1997
IVF	42	0.88	NR	1.15	Lam et al., 1999
IVF	151	0.99	0.94	1.14	Wald et al., 1999b
IVF	70	1.13	0.98	1.31	Bar-Hava et al., 2001
IVF	46	1.04	1.11	1.38	Maymon and Shulman, 2001
IVF	71	1.13	0.94	1.12	Maymon and Shulman, 2002
IVF	58	0.95	NR	1.19	Räty et al., 2002
IVF	96	0.98	NR	1.2	Perheentupa et al., 2002
IVF	970	0.97	0.9	1.1	Muller et al., 2003
IVF	88	0.99	1.12	1.12	Rice et al., 2005
OI	1,632	1.02	0.92	1.09	Barkai et al., 1996
OI+IUI	43	0.76	NR	1.09	Hsu et al., 1999
ICSI	23	0.76	NR	0.88	Lam et al., 1999
ICSI	48	1.22	NR	1.53	Perheentupa et al., 2002
ICSI	545	0.95	1	1.01	Muller et al., 2003
OD	37	1.45	0.97	1.32	Maymon and Shulman, 2001

OI=ovulation induction; IUI=intrauterine insemination; ICSI=intracytoplasmic sperm injection; OD=oocyte donation; AFP=α-fetoprotein; MOM=multiples of the mean; uE3=unconjugated estriol; HCG=human chorionic gonadotrophin; NR=not recorded.

The data concerning maternal serum inhibin levels in ART pregnancies is limited. Wald *et al.* (1999b) found that the median serum inhibin levels in 39 singleton pregnancies conceived by IVF were not significantly different from 195 controls. In contrast, our group (Maymon *et al.*, 2006) found that the median serum inhibin levels of 170 ART singleton pregnancies were significantly higher as compared to 4,334 spontaneous singletons (1.11 MoM versus 0.99 MoM respectively, $P < 0.001$).

Following correction for gestational age by means of dating scan and for maternal age at conception, it was concluded that the high second-trimester FPR in the IVF patients is mainly attributed to factors that are directly associated with the pregnancy itself. These findings support the concept that such pregnancies may have a primary underlying pathology. This may result from various unknown metabolic disturbances in the feto-placental unit to placental-related obstetric complications (Ribbert *et al.*, 1996). Indeed, IVF pregnancies were found to be associated with a higher incidence of low birth weight and premature delivery compared with spontaneous conception (Jackson *et al.*, 2004; Kalra and Molinaro, 2008). These complications are typically predicted and characterized by high maternal serum hCG and AFP (Ogle *et al.*, 2000).

First Trimester Screening

Theoretically, first-trimester screening should be directly influenced by ART, particularly by the hormonal treatments and the presence of multiple corpora lutea. Moreover, the effect of ART is likely to persist throughout the first trimester of gestation. Thus, one would expect that serum marker changes induced by this treatment would be more marked during the first trimester and mainly be reflected by high maternal serum HCG and low PAPP-A (Ben-Ami and Maymon, 2012).

In fact, the effect of ART on first trimester screening is also controversial. As seen in Table 2, most studies of first-trimester screening report decreased PAPP-A levels in IVF pregnancies with unaltered levels of Fβ-hCG (Ogle *et al.*, 2000; Wøjdeman *et al.*, 2001; Jackson *et al.*, 2004; Hui *et al.*, 2005; Kalra and Molinaro, 2008; Engels *et al.*, 2010). However, other authors found decreased PAPP-A levels and increased Fβ-hCG levels (Bellver *et al.*, 2005; Lambert-Messerlian *et al.*, 2006) or decreased Fβ-hCG levels (Hui *et al.*, 2005; Engels *et al.*, 2010), and some show no changes in maternal serum values in IVF pregnancies (Wøjdeman *et al.*, 2001; Bellver *et al.*, 2005; Lambert-

Messerlian *et al.*, 2006). In ICSI pregnancies, a decrease in PAPP-A levels has been reported with unaltered levels of Fβ-hCG (Ogle *et al.*, 2000; Ghisoni *et al.*, 2003; Bellver *et al.*, 2005; Hui *et al.*, 2005; Engels *et al.*, 2010). One study reported increased levels of Fβ-hCG (Ghisoni *et al.*, 2003) and other studies have found no changes in maternal serum values in ICSI pregnancies (Orlandi *et al.*, 2002; Bellver *et al.*, 2005).

Table 2. The biochemistry serum screening profile in pregnancies achieved by ART

Assisted mode of conception	No. of cases	PAPP-A MoM	Fβ-hCG MoM	NT MoM	Reference
IVF	220	1.0	1.21	0.97	Liao *et al.*, 2001
ICSI	30	0.86	1.09	1.00	Liao *et al.*, 2001
OD	161	1.04	0.96	0.96	Liao *et al.*, 2001
IVF	47	1.02	1.14	0.97	Wøjdemann *et al.*, 2001
OI	63	0.89	1.02	1.08	Wøjdemann *et al.*, 2001
IVF	71	0.96	1.16	1.16	Maymon and Shulman, 2002
IVF	203	0.76	0.94	0.94	Engels *et al.*, 2010
ICSI	192	0.71	1.04	0.98	Engels *et al.*, 2010
IVF	47	1.06	0.83	NR	Bellver *et al.*, 2005
ICSI	222	1.13	1.13	NR	Bellver *et al.*, 2005
OI	97	1.26	0.98	NR	Bellver *et al.*, 2005
IVF	277	0.94	1.13	1.03	Lambert-Messerlian *et al.*, 2006
OI	323	0.91	1.06	1.02	Lambert-Messerlian *et al.*, 2006
IUI	247	0.98	1.08	0.97	Lambert-Messerlian *et al.*, 2006
OD	56	1.00	1.22	0.96	Lambert-Messerlian *et al.*, 2006
IVF	92	0.83	0.87	NR	Hui *et al.*, 2005
ICSI	57	0.7	0.82	NR	Hui *et al.*, 2005
IVF	32	0.79	0.84	1.1	Orlandi *et al.*, 2002
ICSI	42	0.96	1.13	1.02	Orlandi *et al.*, 2002
IVF	512	0.78	0.96	1.5	Gjerris *et al.*, 2009b
ICSI	396	0.79	0.98	1.6	Gjerris *et al.*, 2009b

OI=ovulation induction; IUI=intrauterine insemination; ICSI=intracytoplasmic sperm injection; OD=oocyte donation; PAPP-A= pregnancy-associated placental protein-A; NT= nuchal translucency; Fβ-hCG=free β-subunit of human chorionic gonadotrophin; MoM=multiples of the mean; NR=not recorded.

The lower PAPP-A concentrations (range: 0.71-1.13 median MoM, Table 2) might be attributed to early testing in the ART group or might be secondary to early metabolic impairment of the feto-placental unit (Ong *et al.*, 2000). Lower PAPP-A and Fβ-hCG concentrations at 10-14 weeks of gestation were also reported to be associated with the subsequent development of various pregnancy complications (Ong *et al.*, 2000).

In the combined results of all published series (Barkai *et al.*, 1996; Heinonen *et al.*, 1996; Ribbert *et al.*, 1996; Frishman *et al.*, 1997; Hsu *et al.*, 1999; Lam *et al.*, 1999; Wald *et al.*, 1999b; Bar-Hava *et al.*, 2001; Liao *et al.*, 2001; Maymon and Shulman, 2001,2002,2004; Niemimaa *et al.*, 2001; Wøjdemann *et al.*, 2001; Orlandi *et al.*, 2002; Perheentupa *et al.*, 2002; Raty *et al.*, 2002; Lai *et al.*, 2003; Bellver *et al.*, 2005; Hui *et al.*, 2005; Lambert-Messerlian *et al.*, 2006; Tul *et al.*, 2006; Gjerris *et al.*, 2009b), Cuckle and Benn (2010) have reported that the overall mean value for all hCG isoforms was 1.08 MoM and for PAPP-A 0.91 MoM. However, there is considerable heterogeneity between the series, possibly due to the method of gestational assessment, the cause of infertility or the type of therapy, for example whether the oocytes are donated or obtained from the patient, frozen or fresh. The specific hormone treatments or infertility conditions that presumably are the underlying cause of the alteration in the marker levels remains unclear.

In contrast to the fluctuating maternal serum results, NT measurements are found to be more consistent. Indeed, NT thickness does not seem to be affected by ART in most studies (Wøjdeman *et al.*, 2001; Ghisoni *et al.*, 2003; Liao *et al.*, 2001; Maymon and Shulman, 2004). However, some studies have found an increased NT thickness in IVF or ICSI pregnancies (Kalra and Molinaro, 2008; Gjerris *et al.*, 2009b) or a decreased NT thickness (Gjerris *et al.*, 2009b).

Initial data suggest that NB status is independent of serum biochemistry. Although absent NB is associated with increased NT thickness, these ultrasound findings can be combined as long as the calculation of DS risk takes this association into account. Therefore, adding NB assessment to measurements of NT and maternal serum markers has the potential to improve accuracy of risk assessment, and the inclusion of NB likelihood ratios to risk estimates is statistically valid. In a prospective study of a high-risk population with a median maternal age of 35 years assessed by NT, NB, and biochemistry, it was estimated that 93.6% of DS cases would be detected at a FPR of 5% (Cicero *et al.*, 2006). Although these data are promising, they reflect the experience of highly specialized and high-risk centers and are not generalizable to less experienced centers (Rosen *et al.*, 2007).

Sequential Screening

The effect of ART on integrated (first and second trimester) screening was assessed in a group that underwent a serial integrated DS screening test (Maymon and Shulman, 2002). The study protocol included first-trimester combined NT, Fβ-hCG and PAPP-A testing. The second-trimester triple serum screening included AFP, intact hCG and uE_3. After excluding aneuploidies, miscarriages, anatomical anomalies and cases with incomplete follow-up, the serum samples of normal cases were assessed and correlated. NT measurement was not significantly changed in either group. However, the IVF group had lower PAPP-A and higher AFP. Both groups had similar rates of first-trimester FPR, but the IVF group had a significantly higher mid-gestation FPR rate (10 versus 5 %; P=0.029). This has contributed to amniocentesis uptake rates of 15 and 13% for the IVF and natural conception pregnancies, respectively. It was concluded that ART singleton patients should be screened either by the integrated first- and second-trimester screening tests or the use of NT alone (Maymon and Shulman, 2002).

A later report from the same group assessed the profile of markers that constitute the integrated test, measuring its FPR among a preselected group of unaffected IVF pregnancies. These results were compared with the reference laboratory values that reflect the general obstetric population, which underwent the same investigative protocol. The IVF group had significantly lower PAPP-A (0.78 versus 1.03, t-test $P < 0.05$) and higher NT (1.14 versus 1.01, $P < 0.05$) values, respectively. All the other markers were similar for both groups. On the basis of the integrated test, a higher rate of IVF pregnancies were defined as being screen-positive (6.1% vs 3.7%), although the values did not reach a level of statistical significance (Maymon and Shulman, 2004).

Conclusion

It is postulated that DS screening in ART pregnancies is associated with a higher FPR. To decrease the magnitude of such uncertain experience, it is advised to use better screening modalities, such as the combined or integrated tests (Weisz and Rodeck, 2006). In practice, pregnancies achieved by ART receive obstetric care from very early in the first trimester. Therefore, it may be advantageous to offer them NT as the initial DS screening method. In high risk cases, if there is an experienced sonographer, addition of other sonographic markers, such as NB and Doppler flow studies might enhance the detection rate. In centers which still conduct the triple test, when the NT screening is negative, it would then be reasonable to subsequently offer the second trimester serum testing, producing a combined risk assessment. The LR should be applied from the NT screen to the risk from the serum screen or vice versa. One should be able to work out either one or both of the ratios from the reports if they include the age-specific risk (AR) and the final risk (FR) expressed as odds, using the formula : LR=FR/AR (Maymon and Jauniaux, 2002). These calculations assume that the NT measurement was performed using the Fetal Medicine Foundation protocol (Snijders *et al.*, 1998).

The Future...

Nicolaides (2011) has proposed a strategy of first-trimester triage for a wide range of adverse pregnancy outcomes, which he entitles 'a new pyramid of care'. His proposal is to use the results of tests and examinations carried out at the time of first-trimester aneuploidy screening to plan a sequence of further tests and visits tailored to the individual patient. Among them is screening for pre-eclampsia in the first trimester.

Modeling predicts a very high detection rate for the more severe early-onset cases (Akolekar *et al.*, 2011) and meta-analysis indicates that low-dose aspirin halves the incidence of pre-eclampsia if initiated before 16 weeks' gestation (Bujold *et al.*, 2010). While performing NT screening recent reports have shown that early detection of spina bifida is feasible by looking into intracranial translucency (Chaoui *et al.*, 2009; Chaoui and Nicolaides, 2010). This observation is especially important in multiple pregnancies where maternal serum AFP levels are less sensitive for alerting of neural tube defects. In addition, after decades of intensive research with a wide range of putative methodologies, at last a commercially viable technique has emerged to analysed cell free fetal DNA in maternal circulation for the non-invasive prenatal diagnosis (NIPD) of DS and other chromosomal abnormalities (Ehrich *et al.*, 2011; Palomaki *et al.*, 2011; Sehnert *et al.*, 2011). Public health planners and clinicians providing healthcare to individual patients need to evaluate the efficacy of this technique and assess the consequences of this new option (Benn *et al.*, 2012). NIPD for DS could be incorporated in a contingent fashion, for those with intermediate risk following conventional screening, without compromising these new screening approaches. The role or timing of second-trimester ultrasound for the detection of additional fetal anatomic abnormalities and the use of the second-trimester maternal serum AFP test will also need to be re-evaluated. The above mentioned screening algorithm along with those previously reported DS screening tests tailored to mode of conception and number of fetuses may enhance the antenatal care for those assisted iatrogenic pregnancies, while taking into consideration their specific needs and problems.

REFERENCES

Aboulghar H, Aboulghar M, Mansour R, Serour G, Amin Y, Al-Inany H. A prospective controlled study of karyotyping for 430 consecutive babies conceived through intracytoplasmic sperm injection. *Fertil Steril* 2001; 76: 249-253.

Achiron R, Tadmor O, Mashiach S. Heart rate as a predictor of first-trimester spontaneous abortion after ultrasound-proven viability. *Obstet Gynecol* 1991; 78: 330-334.

Akolekar R, Syngelaki A, Sarquis R, Zvanca M, Nicolaides KH. Prediction of early, intermediate and late pre-eclampsia from maternal factors, biophysical and biochemical markers at 11-13 weeks. *Prenat Diagn* 2011; 31: 66-74.

Bar-Hava I, Yitzhak M, Krissi H, Shohat M, Shalev J, Czitron B, Ben-Rafael Z, Orvieto R. Triple-test screening in in vitro fertilization pregnancies. *J Assist Reprod Genet* 2001; 18: 226-229.

Barkai G, Goldman B, Ries L, Chaki R, Dor J, Cuckle H. Down's syndrome screening marker levels following assisted reproduction. *Prenat Diagn* 1996; 16: 1111-1114.

Barton SE, Missmer SA, Hornstein MD. Twin pregnancies with a 'vanished' embryo: a higher risk multiple gestation group? *Hum Reprod*, 2011; 26: 2750-2753.

Bellver J, Lara C, Soares SR, Ramírez A, Pellicer A, Remohí J, Serra V. First trimester biochemical screening for Down's syndrome in singleton pregnancies conceived by assisted reproduction. *Hum Reprod* 2005; 20: 2623-2627.

Benn P, Cuckle H, Pergament E. Opinion: Non-invasive prenatal diagnosis for Down syndrome: the paradigm will shift, but slowly. *Ultrasound Obstet Gynecol* 2012; 39: 127-130.

Ben-Ami I, Maymon R. Prenatal diagnosis after assisted reproductive technology. In: Jauniaux ERM, Rizk BRMB, eds. *Pregnancy after Assisted Reproductive Technology.* Cambridge University Press; 2012; 149-167.

Berkowitz RL, Lynch L, Lapinski R, Bergh P. First-trimester transabdominal multifetal pregnancy reduction: a report of two hundred completed cases. *Am J Obstet Gynecol* 1993; 169: 17-21.

Berkowitz RL, Lynch L, Stone J, Alvarez M. The current status of multifetal pregnancy reduction. *Am J Obstet Gynecol* 1996; 174: 1265-1272.

Bonduelle M, Van Assche E, Joris H, Keymolen K, Devroey P, Van Steirteghem A, Liebaers I. Prenatal testing in ICSI pregnancies: incidence of chromosomal anomalies in 1586 karyotypes and relation to sperm parameters. *Hum Reprod* 2002; 17: 2600-2614.

Borrell A. Promises and pitfalls of first trimester sonographic markers in the detection of fetal aneuploidy. *Prenat Diagn* 2009; 29: 62-68.

Brambati B, Tului L, Baldi M, Guercilena S. Genetic analysis prior to selective fetal reduction in multiple pregnancy: technical aspects and clinical outcome. *Hum Reprod* 1995; 10: 818-825.

Bujold E, Roberge S, Lacasse Y, Bureau M, Audibert F, Marcoux S, Forest JC, Giguère Y. Prevention of preeclampsia and intrauterine growth restriction with aspirin started in early pregnancy: a meta-analysis. *Obstet Gynecol* 2010; 116: 402-414.

Chaoui R, Nicolaides KH. From nuchal translucency to intracranial translucency: towards the early detection of spina bifida. *Ultrasound Obstet Gynecol* 2010; 35: 133-138.

Chaoui R, Benoit B, Mitkowska-Wozniak H, Heling KS, Nicolaides KH. Assessment of intracranial translucency (IT) in the detection of spina bifida at the 11-13-week scan.*Ultrasound Obstet Gynecol* 2009; 34: 249-252.

Chen HJ, Huang LW, Lin YH, Seow KM, Hsieh BC, Hwang JL, Tzeng CR. Midtrimester maternal serum inhibin A levels after multifetal pregnancy reduction. *Prenat Diagn* 2007; 27: 431-434.

Chiu RW, Akolekar R, Zheng YW, Leung TY, Sun H, Chan KC, Lun FM, Go AT, Lau ET, To WW, Leung WC, Tang RY, Au-Yeung SK, Lam H, Kung YY, Zhang X, van Vugt JM, Minekawa R, Tang MH, Wang J, Oudejans CB, Lau TK, Nicolaides KH, Lo YM. Non-invasive prenatal assessment of trisomy 21 by multiplexed maternal plasma DNA sequencing: large scale validity study. *BMJ* 2011; 342: c7401.

Cicero S, Curcio P, Papageorghiou A, Sonek J, Nicolaides K. Absence of nasal bone in fetuses with trisomy 21 at 11-14 weeks of gestation: an observational study. *Lancet* 2001; 358: 1665-1667.

Cicero S, Rembouskos G, Vandecruys H, Hogg M, Nicolaides KH. Likelihood ratio for trisomy 21 in fetuses with absent nasal bone at the 11-14-week scan. *Ultrasound Obstet Gynecol* 2004; 23: 218-223.

Cicero S, Avgidou K, Rembouskos G, Kagan KO, Nicolaides KH. Nasal bone in first-trimester screening for trisomy 21. *Am J Obstet Gynecol* 2006; 195: 109-114

Cleary-Goldman J, Rebarber A, Krantz D, Hallahan T, Saltzman D. First-trimester screening with nasal bone in twins. *Am J Obstet Gynecol* 2008; 199: 283 e1-3.

Cuckle H, Moskovitch M, Vaknin Z, Levental S, Rosen H, Maymon R. Nuchal translucency screening in triplets: Down syndrome risk calculation taking account of between-fetus correlations. *Prenat Diagn* 2012; 32: 214-219.

Cuckle H, Maymon R. Down syndrome risk calculation for a twin fetus taking account of the nuchal translucency in the co-twin. *Prenat Diagn* 2010; 30: 827-833.

Cuckle H, Benn P. Multi-marker maternal serum screening for chromosomal abnormalities. In: Milunsky A, Milunsky JM, eds. *Genetic Disorders and the Fetus: Diagnosis, Prevention and Treatment*. Baltimore: Johns Hopkins University Press; 2010; 771-818.

Cuckle H. Antenatal screening for Down's syndrome. *Lancet* 1998a; 352: 1144-1145.

Cuckle H. Down's syndrome screening in twins. *J Med Screen* 1998b; 5: 3-4.

Cuckle HS. Growing complexity in the choice of Down's syndrome screening policy. *Ultrasound Obstet Gynecol* 2002; 19: 323-326.

De Biasio P, Siccardi M, Volpe G, Famularo L, Santi F, Canini S. First-trimester screening for Down syndrome using nuchal translucency measurement with free beta-hCG and PAPP-A between 10 and 13 weeks of pregnancy--the combined test. *Prenat Diagn* 1999; 19: 360-363.

de Graaf IM, Pajkrt E, Bilardo CM, Leschot NJ, Cuckle HS, van Lith JM. Early pregnancy screening for fetal aneuploidy with serum markers and nuchal translucency. *Prenat Diagn* 1999; 19: 458-462.

Dickey RP, Olar TT, Taylor SN, Curole DN, Rye PH, Matulich EM, Dickey MH. Incidence and significance of unequal gestational sac diameter or embryo crown-rump length in twin pregnancy. *Hum Reprod* 1992; 7: 1170-1172.

Dickey RP, Taylor SN, Lu PY, Sartor BM, Storment JM, Rye PH, Pelletier WD, Zender JL, Matulich EM. Spontaneous reduction of multiple pregnancy: incidence and effect on outcome. *Am J Obstet Gynecol* 2002; 186: 77-83.

Doyle PE, Beral V, Botting B, Wale CJ. Congenital malformations in twins in England and Wales. *J Epidemiol Community Health* 1991; 45: 43-48.

Eddleman KA, Stone JL, Lynch L, Berkowitz RL. Chorionic villus sampling before multifetal pregnancy reduction. *Am J Obstet Gynecol* 2000; 183: 1078-1081.

Ehrich M, Deciu C, Zwiefelhofer T, Tynan JA, Cagasan L, Tim R, Lu V, McCullough R, McCarthy E, Nygren AO, Dean J, Tang L, Hutchison D, Lu T, Wang H, Angkachatchai V, Oeth P, Cantor CR, Bombard A, van den Boom D. Noninvasive detection of fetal trisomy 21 by sequencing of DNA in maternal blood: a study in a clinical setting. *Am J Obstet Gynecol* 2011; 204: 205.e1-11.

Engels MA, Kooij M, Schats R, Twisk JW, Blankenstein MA, van Vugt JM. First-trimester serum marker distribution in singleton pregnancies conceived with assisted reproduction. *Prenat Diagn* 2010; 30: 372-377.

Evans MI, Berkowitz RL, Wapner RJ, Carpenter RJ, Goldberg JD, Ayoub MA, Horenstein J, Dommergues M, Brambati B, Nicolaides KH, Holzgreve W, Timor-Tritsch IE. Improvement in outcomes of multifetal pregnancy reduction with increased experience. *Am J Obstet Gynecol* 2001; 184: 97-103.

Frishman GN, Canick JA, Hogan JW, Hackett RJ, Kellner LH, Saller DN Jr. Serum triple-marker screening in in vitro fertilization and naturally conceived pregnancies. *Obstet Gynecol* 1997; 90: 98-101.

Fukada Y, Yasumizu T, Takizawa M, Amemiya A, Hoshi K. The prognosis of fetuses with transient nuchal translucency in the first and early second trimester. *Acta Obstet Gynecol Scand* 1997; 76: 913-916.

Geipel A, Gembruch U, Ludwig M, Germer U, Schwinger E, Dormeier A, Diedrich K. Genetic sonography as the preferred option of prenatal diagnosis in patients with pregnancies following intracytoplasmic sperm injection. *Hum Reprod* 1999; 14: 2629-2634.

Ghisoni L, Ferrazzi E, Castagna C, Levi Setti PE, Masini AC, Pigni A. Prenatal diagnosis after ART success: the role of early combined screening tests in counselling pregnant patients. *Placenta* 2003; 24: S99-S103.

Gjerris AC, Tabor A, Loft A, Christiansen M, Pinborg A. First trimester prenatal screening among women pregnant after IVF/ICSI. *Hum Reprod Update* 2012; 18: 350-359.

Gjerris AC, Loft A, Pinborg A, Christiansen M, Tabor A. The effect of a 'vanishing twin' on biochemical and ultrasound first trimester screening markers for Down's syndrome in pregnancies conceived by assisted reproductive technology. *Hum Reprod* 2009a; 24: 55-62.

Gjerris AC, Loft A, Pinborg A, Christiansen M, Tabor A. First-trimester screening markers are altered in pregnancies conceived after IVF/ICSI. *Ultrasound Obstet Gynecol* 2009b; 33: 8-17.

Gjerris AC, Loft A, Pinborg A, Christiansen M, Tabor A. Prenatal testing among women pregnant after assisted reproductive techniques in Denmark 1995-2000: a national cohort study. *Hum Reprod* 2008; 23: 1545-1552.

Goncé A, Borrell A, Fortuny A, Casals E, Martínez MA, Mercadé I, Cararach V, Vanrell JA. First-trimester screening for trisomy 21 in twin pregnancy: does the addition of biochemistry make an improvement? *Prenat Diagn* 2005; 25: 1156-1161.

Grau P, Robinson L, Tabsh K, Crandall BF. Elevated maternal serum alpha-fetoprotein and amniotic fluid alpha-fetoprotein after multifetal pregnancy reduction. *Obstet Gynecol* 1990; 76: 1042-1045.

Greenwol N, Jauniaux E. Collection of villous tissue under ultrasound guidance to improve the cytogenetic study of early pregnancy failure. *Hum Reprod* 2002; 17: 452-456.

Groutz A, Amit A, Yaron Y, Yovel I, Wolman I, Legum C, Lessing JB. Second-trimester maternal serum alpha-fetoprotein, human chorionic gonadotropin, and unconjugated oestriol after early transvaginal multifetal pregnancy reduction. *Prenat Diagn* 1996; 16: 723-727.

Haddow JE, Palomaki GE, Knight GJ, Williams J, Miller WA, Johnson A. Screening of maternal serum for fetal Down's syndrome in the first trimester. *N Engl J Med* 1998; 338: 955-961.

Heinonen S, Ryynänen M, Kirkinen P, Hippeläinen M, Saarikoski S. Effect of in vitro fertilization on human chorionic gonadotropin serum concentrations and Down's syndrome screening. *Fertil Steril* 1996; 66: 398-403.

Hsu TY, Ou CY, Hsu JJ, Kung FT, Chang SY, Soong YK. Maternal serum screening for down syndrome in pregnancies conceived by intra-uterine insemination. *Prenat Diagn* 1999; 19: 1012-1014.

Hui PW, Lam YH, Tang MH, NG EH, Yeung WS, Ho PC. Maternal serum pregnancy-associated plasma protein-A and free beta-human chorionic gonadotrophin in pregnancies conceived with fresh and frozen-thawed embryos from in vitro fertilization and intracytoplasmic sperm injection. *Prenat Diagn* 2005; 25: 390-393.

Jackson RA, Gibson KA, Wu YW, Croughan MS. Perinatal outcomes in singletons following in vitro fertilization: a meta-analysis. *Obstet Gynecol* 2004; 103: 551-563.

Jauniaux E, Elkazen N, Leroy F, Wilkin P, Rodesch F, Hustin J. Clinical and morphologic aspects of the vanishing twin phenomenon. *Obstet Gynecol* 1988; 72: 577-581.

Jauniaux E, Van Oppenraaij RH, Burton GJ. Obstetric outcome after early placental complications. *Curr Opin Obstet Gynecol* 2010; 22: 452-457.

Jozwiak EA, Ulug U, Mesut A, Erden HF, Bahçeci M. Prenatal karyotypes of fetuses conceived by intracytoplasmic sperm injection. *Fertil Steril* 2004; 82: 628-633.

Kalra SK, Molinaro TA. The association of in vitro fertilization and perinatal morbidity. *Semin Reprod Med* 2008; 26: 423-435.

Kelly MP, Molo MW, Maclin VM, Binor Z, Rawlins RG, Radwanska E. Human chorionic gonadotropin rise in normal and vanishing twin pregnancies. *Fertil Steril* 1991; 56: 221-224.

Kidd SA, Lancaster PA, Anderson JC, Boogert A, Fisher CC, Robertson R, Wass DM. A cohort study of pregnancy outcome after amniocentesis in twin pregnancy. *Paediatr Perinat Epidemiol* 1997; 11: 200-213.

Koster MP, Wortelboer EJ, Stoutenbeek P, Visser GH, Schielen PC. Distributions of current and new first-trimester Down syndrome screening markers in twin pregnancies. *Prenat Diagn* 2010; 30: 413-417.

Krantz DA, Hallahan TW, He K, Sherwin JE, Evans MI. First-trimester screening in triplets. *Am J Obstet Gynecol* 2011; 205: 364.

Lai TH, Chen SC, Tsai MS, Lee FK, Wei CF. First-trimester screening for Down syndrome in singleton pregnancies achieved by intrauterine insemination. *J Assist Reprod Genet* 2003; 20: 327-331.

Lam YH, Yeung WS, Tang MH, Ng EH, So WW, Ho PC. Maternal serum alpha-fetoprotein and human chorionic gonadotrophin in pregnancies conceived after intracytoplasmic sperm injection and conventional in-vitro fertilization. *Hum Reprod* 1999; 14: 2120-2123.

Lambert-Messerlian G, Dugoff L, Vidaver J, Canick JA, Malone FD, Ball RH, Comstock CH, Nyberg DA, Saade G, Eddleman K, Klugman S, Craigo SD, Timor-Tritsch IE, Carr SR, Wolfe HM, D'Alton ME. First- and second-trimester Down syndrome screening markers in pregnancies achieved through assisted reproductive technologies (ART): a FASTER trial study. *Prenat Diagn* 2006; 26: 672-678.

Landy HJ, Keith LG. The vanishing twin: a review. *Hum Reprod Update* 1998; 4: 177-183.

Liao AW, Heath V, Kametas N, Spencer K, Nicolaides KH. First-trimester screening for trisomy 21 in singleton pregnancies achieved by assisted reproduction. *Hum Reprod* 2001; 16: 1501-1504.

Linskens IH, Spreeuwenberg MD, Blankenstein MA, van Vugt JM. Early first-trimester free beta-hCG and PAPP-A serum distributions in monochorionic and dichorionic twins. *Prenat Diagn* 2009; 29: 74-78.

Lipitz S, Shulman A, Achiron R, Zalel Y, Seidman DS. A comparative study of multifetal pregnancy reduction from triplets to twins in the first versus early second trimesters after detailed fetal screening. *Ultrasound Obstet Gynecol* 2001; 18: 35-38.

Lynch L, Berkowitz RL. Maternal serum alpha-fetoprotein and coagulation profiles after multifetal pregnancy reduction. *Am J Obstet Gynecol* 1993; 169: 987-990.

Madsen HN, Ball S, Wright D, Tørring N, Petersen OB, Nicolaides KH, Spencer K. A reassessment of biochemical marker distributions in trisomy 21-affected and unaffected twin pregnancies in the first trimester. *Ultrasound Obstet Gynecol* 2011; 37: 38-47.

Maiz N, Staboulidou I, Leal AM, Minekawa R, Nicolaides KH. Ductus venosus Doppler at 11 to 13 weeks of gestation in the prediction of outcome in twin pregnancies. *Obstet Gynecol* 2009; 113: 860-865.

Marrs RP, Kletzky OA, Howard WF, Mishell DR Jr. Disappearance of human chorionic gonadotropin and resumption of ovulation following abortion. *Am J Obstet Gynecol* 1979; 135: 731-736.

Maslovitz S, Yaron Y, Fait G, Gull I, Wolman I, Jaffa A, Hartoov J. Feasibility of nuchal translucency in triplet pregnancies. *J Ultrasound Med* 2004; 23: 501-504.

Maymon R, Herman A. Multifetal pregnancy reduction. *Am J Obstet Gynecol* 2001; 185: 772-774.

Maymon R, Shulman A. Integrated first- and second-trimester Down syndrome screening test among unaffected IVF pregnancies. *Prenat Diagn* 2004; 24: 125-129.

Maymon R, Shulman A. Serial first- and second-trimester Down's syndrome screening tests among IVF-versus naturally-conceived singletons. *Hum Reprod* 2002; 17: 1081-1085.

Maymon R, Shulman A. Comparison of triple serum screening and pregnancy outcome in oocyte donation versus IVF pregnancies. *Hum Reprod* 2001; 16: 691-695.

Maymon R, Jauniaux E. Down's syndrome screening in pregnancies after assisted reproductive techniques: an update. *Reprod Biomed Online* 2002; 4: 285-293.

Maymon R, Rosen H, Baruchin O, Herman A, Cuckle H. Model predicted Down syndrome detection rates for nuchal translucency screening in twin pregnancies. *Prenat Diagn* 2011; 31: 426-429.

Maymon R, Cuckle H, Herman A. Maternal serum inhibin levels in twin and singleton pregnancies conceived by assisted reproduction. *Hum Reprod* 2006; 21: 1305-1308.

Maymon R, Rosen H, Baruchin O, Herman A, Cuckle H. Current concepts of Down syndrome screening tests in assisted reproduction twin pregnancies: another double trouble. *Prenat Diagn* 2005; 25: 746-750.

Maymon R, Jauniaux E, Holmes A, Wiener YM, Dreazen E, Herman A. Nuchal translucency measurement and pregnancy outcome after assisted conception versus spontaneously conceived twins. *Hum Reprod* 2001; 16: 1999-2004.

Maymon R, Dreazen E, Rozinsky S, Bukovsky I, Weinraub Z, Herman A. Comparison of nuchal translucency measurement and mid-gestation serum screening in assisted reproduction versus naturally conceived singleton pregnancies. *Prenat Diagn* 1999a; 19: 1007-1011.

Maymon R, Dreazen E, Tovbin Y, Bukovsky I, Weinraub Z, Herman A. The feasibility of nuchal translucency measurement in higher order multiple gestations achieved by assisted reproduction. *Hum Reprod* 1999b; 14: 2102-2105.

Maymon R, Dreazen E, Rozinsky S, Bukovsky I, Weinraub Z, Herman A. Comparison of nuchal translucency measurement and second-trimester triple serum screening in twin versus singleton pregnancies. *Prenat Diagn* 1999c; 19: 727-731.

Maymon R, Herman A, Shulman A, Halperin R, Arieli S, Bukovsky I, Weinraub Z. First trimester embryo reduction: a medical solution to an iatrogenic problem. *Hum Reprod* 1995; 10: 668-673.

Monni G, Zoppi MA, Cau G, Lai R, Baldi M. Importance of nuchal translucency measurement in multifetal pregnancy reduction. *Ultrasound Obstet Gynecol* 1999; 13: 377-378.

Muller F, Dreux S, Lemeur A, Sault C, Desgrès J, Bernard MA, Giorgetti C, Lemay C, Mirallié S, Beauchet A; French Collaborative Group. Medically assisted reproduction and second-trimester maternal serum marker screening for Down syndrome. *Prenat Diagn* 2003; 23: 1073-1076.

Nicolaides KH. A model for a new pyramid of prenatal care based on the 11 to 13 weeks' assessment. *Prenat Diagn* 2011; 31: 3-6.

Niemimaa M, Heinonen S, Seppälä M, Hippeläinen M, Martikainen H, Ryynänen M. First-trimester screening for Down's syndrome in in vitro fertilization pregnancies. *Fertil Steril* 2001; 76: 1282-1283.

Ogle R, Jauniaux E, Pahal GS, Dell E, Sheldrake A, Rodeck C. Serum screening for Down syndrome and adverse pregnancy outcomes: a case-controlled study. *Prenat Diagn* 2000: 20: 96-99.

Ong CY, Liao AW, Spencer K, Munim S, Nicolaides KH. First trimester maternal serum free beta human chorionic gonadotrophin and pregnancy associated plasma protein A as predictors of pregnancy complications. *BJOG* 2000; 107: 1265-1270.

Orlandi F, Rossi C, Allegra A, Krantz D, Hallahan T, Orlandi E, Macri J. First trimester screening with free beta-hCG, PAPP-A and nuchal translucency in pregnancies conceived with assisted reproduction. *Prenat Diagn* 2002; 22: 718-721.

Palomaki GE, Kloza EM, Lambert-Messerlian GM, Haddow JE, Neveux LM, Ehrich M, van den Boom D, Bombard AT, Deciu C, Grody WW, Nelson SF, Canick JA. DNA sequencing of maternal plasma to detect Down syndrome: an international clinical validation study. *Genet Med* 2011; 13: 913-920.

Pandya PP, Snijders RJ, Johnson SP, De Lourdes Brizot M, Nicolaides KH. Screening for fetal trisomies by maternal age and fetal nuchal translucency thickness at 10 to 14 weeks of gestation. *Br J Obstet Gynaecol* 1995a; 102: 957-962.

Pandya PP, Hilbert F, Snijders RJ, Nicolaides KH. Nuchal translucency thickness and crown-rump length in twin pregnancies with chromosomally abnormal fetuses. *J Ultrasound Med* 1995b; 14: 565-568.

Perheentupa A, Ruokonen A, Tuomivaara L, Ryynänen M, Martikainen H. Maternal serum beta-HCG and alpha-fetoprotein concentrations in singleton pregnancies following assisted reproduction. *Hum Reprod* 2002; 17: 794-797.

Pinborg A, Loft A, Rasmussen S, Schmidt L, Langhoff-Roos J, Greisen G, Andersen AN. Neonatal outcome in a Danish national cohort of 3438 IVF/ICSI and 10,362 non-IVF/ICSI twins born between 1995 and 2000. *Hum Reprod* 2004; 19: 435-441.

Prats P, Rodríguez I, Nicolau J, Comas C. Early first-trimester free-beta-hCG and PAPP-A serum distributions in monochorionic and dichorionic twins. *Prenat Diagn* 2012; 32: 64-69.

Räty R, Virtanen A, Koskinen P, Anttila L, Forsström J, Laitinen P, Mörsky P, Tiitinen A, Ekblad U. Serum free beta-HCG and alpha-fetoprotein levels in IVF, ICSI and frozen embryo transfer pregnancies in maternal mid-trimester serum screening for Down's syndrome. *Hum Reprod* 2002; 17: 481-484.

Räty R, Virtanen A, Koskinen P, Anttila L, Laitinen P, Tiitinen A, Ekblad U. Maternal serum beta-hCG levels in screening for Down syndrome are higher in singleton pregnancies achieved with ovulation induction and intrauterine insemination than in spontaneous singleton pregnancies. *Fertil Steril* 2001; 76: 1075-1077.

Räty R, Virtanen A, Koskinen P, Laitinen P, Forsström J, Salonen R, Mörsky P, Ekblad U. Maternal midtrimester serum AFP and free beta-hCG levels in in vitro fertilization twin pregnancies. *Prenat Diagn* 2000; 20: 221-223.

Reynders CS, Pauker SP, Benacerraf BR. First trimester isolated fetal nuchal lucency: significance and outcome. *J Ultrasound Med* 1997; 16: 101-105.

Ribbert LS, Kornman LH, De Wolf BT, Simons AH, Jansen CA, Beekhuis JR, Mantingh A. Maternal serum screening for fetal Down syndrome in IVF pregnancies. *Prenat Diagn* 1996; 16: 35-38.

Rice JD, McIntosh SF, Halstead AC. Second-trimester maternal serum screening for Down syndrome in in vitro fertilization pregnancies. *Prenat Diagn* 2005; 25: 234-238.

Rosen T, D'Alton ME, Platt LD, Wapner R; Nuchal Translucency Oversight Committee, Maternal Fetal Medicine Foundation. First-trimester ultrasound assessment of the nasal bone to screen for aneuploidy. *Obstet Gynecol* 2007; 110: 399-404.

Rotmensch S, Celentano C, Shalev J, Vishne TH, Lipitz S, Ben-Rafael Z, Glezerman M. Midtrimester maternal serum screening after multifetal pregnancy reduction in pregnancies conceived by in vitro fertilization. *J Assist Reprod Genet* 1999; 16: 8-12.

Sebire NJ, Souka A, Skentou H, Geerts L, Nicolaides KH. Early prediction of severe twin-to-twin transfusion syndrome. *Hum Reprod* 2000; 15: 2008-2010.

Sebire NJ, Snijders RJ, Hughes K, Sepulveda W, Nicolaides KH. Screening for trisomy 21 in twin pregnancies by maternal age and fetal nuchal translucency thickness at 10-14 weeks of gestation. *Br J Obstet Gynaecol* 1996; 103: 999-1003.

Sehnert AJ, Rhees B, Comstock D, de Feo E, Heilek G, Burke J, Rava RP. Optimal detection of fetal chromosomal abnormalities by massively parallel DNA sequencing of cell-free fetal DNA from maternal blood. *Clin Chem* 2011; 57: 1042-1049.

Selam B, Torok O, Lembet A, Stone J, Lapinski R, Berkowitz RL. Genetic amniocentesis after multifetal pregnancy reduction. *Am J Obstet Gynecol* 1999; 180: 226-230.

Sepulveda W, Wong AE, Casasbuenas A. Nuchal translucency and nasal bone in first-trimester ultrasound screening for aneuploidy in multiple pregnancies. *Ultrasound Obstet Gynecol* 2009; 33: 152-156.

Sepulveda W. Chorionicity determination in twin pregnancies: double trouble. *Ultrasound Obstet Gynecol* 1997: 10: 79-81.

Sepulveda W, Sebire NJ, Odibo A, Psarra A, Nicolaides KH. Prenatal determination of chorionicity in triplet pregnancy by ultrasonographic examination of the ipsilon zone. *Obstet Gynecol* 1996; 88: 855-858.

Shetty A, Smith AP. The sonographic diagnosis of chorionicity. *Prenat Diagn* 2005; 25: 735-739.

Shulman A, Maymon R. Mid-gestation Down syndrome screening test and pregnancy outcome among unstimulated assisted-conception pregnancies. *Prenat Diagn* 2003; 23: 625-628.

Shulman LP, Phillips OP. Re: Second-trimester maternal serum alpha-fetoprotein, human chorionic gonadotropin, and unconjugated oestriol after early transvaginal multifetal pregnancy reduction. *Prenat Diagn* 1997; 17: 488-490.

Shulman LP, Phillips OP, Cervetti TA. Maternal serum analyte levels after first-trimester multifetal pregnancy reduction. *Am J Obstet Gynecol* 1996; 174: 1072-1074.

Snijders RJ, Noble P, Sebire N, Souka A, Nicolaides KH. UK multicentre project on assessment of risk of trisomy 21 by maternal age and fetal nuchal-translucency thickness at 10-14 weeks of gestation. Fetal Medicine Foundation First Trimester Screening Group. *Lancet* 1998; 352: 343-346.

Spencer K. Screening for trisomy 21 in twin pregnancies in the first trimester: does chorionicity impact on maternal serum free beta-hCG or PAPP-A levels? *Prenat Diagn* 2001; 21: 715-717.

Spencer K. Screening for trisomy 21 in twin pregnancies in the first trimester using free beta-hCG and PAPP-A, combined with fetal nuchal translucency thickness. *Prenat Diagn* 2000; 20: 91-95.

Spencer K, Nicolaides KH. Screening for trisomy 21 in twins using first trimester ultrasound and maternal serum biochemistry in a one-stop clinic: a review of three years experience. *BJOG* 2003; 110: 276-280.

Spencer K, Kagan KO, Nicolaides KH. Screening for trisomy 21 in twin pregnancies in the first trimester: an update of the impact of chorionicity on maternal serum markers. *Prenat Diagn* 2008; 28: 49-52.

Spencer K, Souter V, Tul N, Snijders R, Nicolaides KH. A screening program for trisomy 21 at 10-14 weeks using fetal nuchal translucency, maternal serum free beta-human chorionic gonadotropin and pregnancy-associated plasma protein-A. *Ultrasound Obstet Gynecol* 1999; 13: 231-237.

Spencer K, Salonen R, Muller F. Down's syndrome screening in multiple pregnancies using alpha-fetoprotein and free beta hCG. *Prenat Diagn* 1994; 14: 537-542.

Szabo J, Gellen J. Nuchal fluid accumulation in trisomy-21 detected by vaginosonography in first trimester. *Lancet* 1990; 336: 1133.

Tul N, Novak-Antolic Z. Serum PAPP-A levels at 10-14 weeks of gestation are altered in women after assisted conception. *Prenat Diagn* 2006; 26: 1206-1211.

Van Lith JM, Pratt JJ, Beekhuis JR, Mantingh A. Second-trimester maternal serum immunoreactive inhibin as a marker for fetal Down's syndrome. *Prenat Diagn* 1992; 12: 801-806.

Wald NJ, Huttly WJ, Hackshaw AK. Antenatal screening for Down's syndrome with the quadruple test. *Lancet* 2003a; 361: 835-836.

Wald NJ, Rish S, Hackshaw AK. Combining nuchal translucency and serum markers in prenatal screening for Down syndrome in twin pregnancies. *Prenat Diagn* 2003b; 23: 588-592.

Wald NJ, Watt HC, Hackshaw AK. Integrated screening for Down's syndrome on the basis of tests performed during the first and second trimesters. *N Engl J Med*, 1999a; 341: 461-467.

Wald NJ, White N, Morris JK, Huttly WJ, Canick JA. Serum markers for Down's syndrome in women who have had in vitro fertilisation: implications for antenatal screening. *Br J Obstet Gynaecol* 1999b; 106: 1304-1306.

Wald NJ, Hackshaw AK. Combining ultrasound and biochemistry in first-trimester screening for Down's syndrome. *Prenat Diagn* 1997; 17: 821-829.

Wald NJ, Kennard A, Hackshaw A, McGuire A. Antenatal screening for Down's syndrome. *J Med Screen* 1997; 4: 181-246.

Wald N, Cuckle H, Wu TS, George L. Maternal serum unconjugated oestriol and human chorionic gonadotrophin levels in twin pregnancies: implications for screening for Down's syndrome. *Br J Obstet Gynaecol* 1991; 98: 905-908.

Weisz B, Rodeck CH. An update on antenatal screening for Down's syndrome and specific implications for assisted reproduction pregnancies. *Hum Reprod* Update 2006; 12: 513-518.

Wenstrom KD, Syrop CH, Hammitt DG, Van Voorhis BJ. Increased risk of monochorionic twinning associated with assisted reproduction. *Fertil Steril* 1993; 60: 510-514.

Wøjdemann KR, Larsen SO, Shalmi AC, Sundberg K, Tabor A, Christiansen M. Nuchal translucency measurements are highly correlated in both mono- and dichorionic twin pairs. *Prenat Diagn* 2006; 26: 218-220.

Wøjdemann KR, Larsen SO, Shalmi A, Sundberg K, Christiansen M, Tabor A. First trimester screening for Down syndrome and assisted reproduction: no basis for concern. *Prenat Diagn* 2001; 21: 563-565.

Zoppi MA, Ibba RM, Axiana C, Floris M, Manca F, Monni G. Absence of fetal nasal bone and aneuploidies at first-trimester nuchal translucency screening in unselected pregnancies. *Prenat Diagn* 2003; 23: 496-500.

In: Advances in Reproductive Technology ...   ISBN: 978-1-62417-875-7
Editor: Ignatz Sanger   © 2013 Nova Science Publishers, Inc.

Chapter 3

SEXED SEMEN TECHNOLOGY IN BUFFALO (BUBALUS BUBALIS) BREEDING AND REPRODUCTIVE TECHNOLOGIES

Giorgio A. Presicce[1] and Giuseppe Campanile[2]
[1]ARSIAL – Regione Lazio, Rome, Italy
[2]DISCIZIA, School of Veterinary Medicine, University of Naples
"Federico II", Naples, Italy

1. SUMMARY

Sexed semen technology has been proved feasible in a number of animal species and in cattle breeding, has especially found economically viable application. In less than 10 years, the same technology has been put to the test in the buffalo species, following detection of buffalo sex chromosomes by fluorescence in situ hybridization (FISH) by using specific X- and Y- probe set derived from flow sorted yak chromosomes, therefore showing the evolutionary conservation of such locus in the water buffalo chromosomes. Considering that in the buffaloes, natural mating is still worldwide the most commonly used strategy adopted for breeding, it is extraordinary that in a relatively short period of time the adoption of sexed semen technology in the same species has given such powerful evidence of efficiency and applicability under farm conditions. Despite the lack of long time selection of bulls for semen selection and freazibility in this species, in recent years some pedigree bulls have been identified and properly selected for semen characteristics and quality.

This has led to the first indisputable evidence and effectiveness of the sexed semen technology in buffaloes through AI, in the year 2004. Within the same study, purity of sorted semen (X-bearing spermatozoa) was found to be similar to what already reported in cattle, and pregnancy rates following deposition of reduced concentration of sexed semen (4 x 10^6) near the utero-tubal junction through use of a special catheter, were reported similar to rates derived from the use of unsorted semen at full dose in similar animals. Subsequently and more recently, both nulliparous and pluriparous buffaloes have been used for AI with an even lower concentration of sexed semen (2 x 10^6), reporting satisfying pregnancy rates similar to those derived from animals following use of unsorted semen. More importantly, in these last trials, deposition of sexed semen has been carried out without the need of special uterine catheters, but rather with a conventional AI gun by emptying the straw at the very beginning of the uterine horn ispilateral to the ovary bearing the preovulatory follicle. More recently, similar satisfying results from the use of sexed semen through AI have been reported in Murrah and Nili Ravi buffaloes too. Furthermore, in the same latter breeds of river buffaloes, sexed spermatozoa have been used and included into in vitro fertilization procedures, giving rise to developing blastocysts and calves born following transfer into selected and synchronized recipients. The evidence provided from the above mentioned studies are of strong encouragement for further research and wider field application of the sexed semen technology in the buffalo species.

2. MALE FEATURES

2.1. Bull: Male Function

In buffalo bulls, likewise cattle bulls, knowledge of morphology, size and scrotal circumference is of paramount importance to determine to a large extent the reproductive efficiency and to predict the potential for semen production. Testicular weight, a reliable index of semen producing ability, has been shown to increase between 2.5 to 3.0 (68.5 g), 3.5 to 4.0 (96.2 g) and 4.5 to 5.0 (114.2 g) years of age (El-Azab et al., 1978). Variations in testes weight are markedly greater among younger bulls and decrease with advancement of age. Paired testes weight is highly correlated with body weight, and there is evidence that larger, faster gaining bulls will have larger testes than smaller bulls of comparable age. As with other animal species, gonadal sperm numbers are positively and significantly correlated with the weight of testicular parenchyma (Abdou et al., 1982; Pant et al., 2003). Moreover, sperm number per gram of testicular parenchyma is much higher at 3.5 to 4 years (85.8 million) and 4.5 to 5 years (75.7 million) than at 2.5 to 3 years (50.7 million). A buffalo bull produces, on average, slightly less than 3 billion of spermatozoa daily and the daily production per gram of testicular parenchyma is about 14 million of sperm cells. The parenchymal sperm concentration per weight does not vary appreciably among ages, indicating that 2 to 3 year-old bulls have already attained the mature rate of spermatogenesis. Nevertheless, variations among bulls appears to decrease with advancement of age, whereas daily sperm production increases markedly with age. In addition, knowledge of morphological features of the testis is instrumental for the evaluation of the influence that different factors, such as the hormonal fluctuations linked to the photo-neuroendocrine system, may have on reproductive efficiency (Seren and Parmeggiani, 1997). The function of the male gonads too, is influenced by the melatonin hormone as the endocrine signal that marks the light and dark hour fluctuation of the day. Such multistep neural pathway is characterized by a domino effect cascade starting with a photoperiod sensitivity to the length and density of the light source, following involvement of the retina, the suprachiasmatic nucleus, the superior cervical ganglia and finally the pineal gland leading to incretion of melatonin. Such neuronal stimulus triggers the rhythmus of melatonin incretion which regulates hypothalamo-hypophysial activity, gonadal function and finally sperm composition and quality (Zicarelli, 1997). Buffalo bulls are characterized by a slower sexual development when compared to cattle bulls. Differentiation of Leydig cells precedes the onset of spermatogonial mitosis, and it seems likely that the production of testosterone by newly differentiated Leydig cells of the prepubertal testis is a prerequisite for initiating spermatogenesis (Rana and Bilaspuri, 2000). Such viability is already very good at this age, allowing for possible processing of spermatozoa for sexing and freezing (Presicce et al., 2005a). While Swamp buffalo bulls may reach ~ 26 cm in scrotal circumference at the age of 24 months (Bongso et al., 1984), Indian and Mediterranean breeds exceeds such value by approximately 10 cm, reaching at the same age 34 to 36 cm (Vale et al., 2001). Interestingly, and in consideration of the seasonal fluctuation in reproductive efficiency in buffalo bulls as well, both weight and size of scrotal circumference together with epididymal weight, are slightly but not significantly reduced in the course of the non-mating season when compared to the mating season (Ibrahim, 1985). Even more interesting is the finding related to the histological evaluation of seminiferous tubules which showed a maintained spermatogenesis during the non-mating season, and more importantly, a significantly higher epithelial lining, indicative of a possible enhancement of function due to the pressure of sperm accumulation, which is typical of this part of the epididymis (Arrighi et al., 2010). Collectively, these findings suggest and confirm the potential of buffalo bulls to breed throughout the year, although reproductive function is somewhat compromised during the non-mating season, as confirmed by a large variability in semen quality reported among Nili-Ravi, Murrah and Mediterranean Italian buffaloes (Kumar et al., 1993; Presicce et al., 2003; Saeed et al., 1990). These considerable differences may be explained by the lack of long time selection for semen freezability in this species. Evaluation of quality of buffalo semen follows the usual guidelines adopted for other large ruminants and especially cattle. In comparison to cattle, where a longer tradition for selection of bulls across the years can be acknowledged, buffalo bulls have begun to be selected for breeding purposes through AI only in the past few decades. As a consequence, the wide range of variation noted above, along a number of semen variables still accounts for a needed stringent selection of buffalo bulls, like the percentage of abnormal sperm cells found in the ejaculate which is an important feature if the final aim is to freeze semen samples. Seasonal and climatic factors have a strong effect on the morphological and chemical seminal characteristics and vary across Countries and latitudes. In temperate regions, it has been reported that better quality semen is produced during spring and winter, while deterioration in semen quality during summer and autumn has been observed. On the other hand, in tropical regions the quality of semen is found to be good during the rainy season whereas in warm and humid tropical Amazon region, the best time to work with semen freezing is between January and June., . In addition to semen quality and its freezability, photoperiod has also been reported to affect sexual activity and bull libido (Sansone et al., 2000). Furthermore, to underline the sensitivity to seasonality in the buffalo species and in particular in the bull, it has been reported a neuro-endocrine interaction between androgen hormones and the autonomic nerve supply in the regulation of male buffalo reproductive functions. In fact, during the mating period, a dense noradrenergic innervations can be observed to supply the vas deferens as well as the accessory sex glands, whereas during the non-mating period the noadrenergic nerves are dramatically and significantly reduced (Mirabella et al., 2007). The puberty in buffalo bull is as variable as in the female and is determined more by body weight than by age. In healthy bulls, testicular spermatogenic cell divisions starts by approximately 12 months of age and active spermatogenesis can be ascertained from 15 months of age. Although it is reported that the ejaculates contain viable spermatozoa only after 24-30 months of age (Perera, 1999), it is not rare to found sexual

mature bulls yet at 15 months. In any case, it seems that buffalo bulls mature more slowly than cattle and have longer time lag between the achievement of puberty and the onset of spermatogenesis.

2.2. Quality and Biochemical Characteristics of Buffalo Semen

Minimal standards for a classification of "probably fertile" specimen of buffalo semen are: a) over $500.000/mm^3$ spermatozoa; b) more than 60% of motile sperm with forward progression and c) more than 70% of the spermatozoa conform to normal morphology. Normal buffalo sperm concentration shows a wide range of variation (600.000 to 1.200.000 cells per mL, and 800.000 per mL on average) and this parameter is highly sensitive to seasonal and nutritional factors. Usually, first ejaculate contains higher number of spermatozoa per mL compared to following ones. Buffalo spermatozoa have distinct morphological features. They are shorter than that of Bos taurus and measure about 62 microns. The mean head length, maximum head breadth and breadth at the base of the head are reported to be 7.20, 4.45, 2.40 microns, respectively. Head area is between 24.3 and 26.6 sq. microns and head shape index 1.62. Various characteristics of buffalo spermatozoa are affected by seasons, feeding regime and sequence of ejaculation (El-Azab, 1980). Freshly collected buffalo semen usually displays a wide range of pH (6.5 to 7.2). Although buffalo ejaculate has a lower concentration of sugars, the built up of lactic acid can decrease semen pH. In addition, seasonal and climatic factors have a strong effect on the morphological and chemical seminal characteristics. Buffaloes are sensitive to heat stress, thus decline in semen quality is a common finding during the hot season of the year. The best manner to overcome the problem of semen quality deterioration due to heat stress during summer is to sprinkle the animals with water during the hotter part of the day or allow the animals to wallow, protect the animals from radiation exchange and hot wind, and keep the animals in ventilated paddock. Free access of the animal to water and shadow is very important, since buffalo have a poorly-developed thermo-regulatory system, causing them to suffer of heat stress during summer.

2.3. Semen Freezability

Freezability of buffalo semen does not seem to be influenced by bull by extender interaction (Ziada, 1992; Ziada et al., 1995). On the other hand season affects buffalo semen freezability. A significant season by bull interaction exists, but not all the bulls are similarly affected by the season effect. Although the equilibration nullifies this effect, freezing and thawing operations exert definite effects on post-thawing sperm recovery. Comparatively better post-thawing motility has been observed in winter and summer collections. Autumn semen is relatively less freezable. Post-thawing acrosomal maintenance, on the other hand, is optimal in winter. Buffalo spermatozoa are very fragile when compared to cattle, and therefore they must be handled with particular care. Since the discovery that buffalo spermatozoa could be cryopreserved, rigorous efforts have been made to predict their freezability on physical, morphological, biological, biochemical bases. The tests used for buffalo semen are essentially those available for bovine semen. These include mainly detection of the susceptibility of spermatozoa to cold effects by determining the percentage of motile spermatozoa, monitoring some valuable parameters as freeze-injury of acrosomal membranes, leakage of acrosomal enzymes as acrosin, hyaluronidase and transaminases. Cold shock inflicted upon buffalo spermatozoa causes changes in the percentage of individually motile spermatozoa, percentage of damaged acrosome, amount of extracellular GOT released comparable to those which take place upon freezing and thawing (El-Sheltawi et al., 1995). However, in view of the extremely low associated variance ($r^2\%$) calculated between various semen parameters (7.29-9.61%), the use of cold shock test to predict freezability of buffalo semen has been considered questionable. The lack of selection for freezability of buffalo bull spermatozoa over the years has been demonstrated by differential staining using Trypan Blu and Giemsa buffalo spermatozoa (Figure 1), to evaluate the integrity of acrosome, tail and midpiece (Presicce et al., 2003; Boccia et al., 2007). Such studies have demonstrated a large variation among bulls used in genetic centers for semen collection and commercial distribution for AI. A semen of high quality collected from bulls of superior genetics is mandatory then, if the same good quality has to be maintained throughout the entire process from sorting to freezing and thawing before AI. Quality can be monitored from collected semen verifying, starting from purity of the two sperm cell populations, progressive linear motility, membrane integrity (propidium iodide test) and osmotic resistance (Campanile et al., 2011). In addition, some authors have suggested to adjust the sperm

concentration per straw up to 2 million living sexed sperm, rather than relying on the total number of sperm cells (Rath et al., 2009).

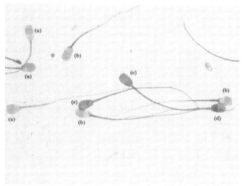

Presicce et al., 2003.

Figure 1. a) unstained head and tail, intact acrosome; b) unstained, stained tail, intact acrosome; d) stained head, unstained tail, intact acrosome; e) stained head and tail, loose acrosome.

3. SEXED SEMEN

Philosophers and poets were the first to digress on the possibility to obtain progeny of the desired sex. A couple of thousand years later, probably the first in depth evaluation of the state of the art of sex control and gender predetermination and the economic value of its successful application, was addressed in a symposium edited by Kiddy and Hafs (1971). An additional decade later, a robust and reliable report on the state of the art in fields bearing sex control was published and edited by Amann and Seidel (1982). On that occasion, historical approaches, including the search for physical, biochemical, and immunological differences, have been discussed, together with the evaluation of methods developed until then that attempt X and Y sperm cell separation, like albumin gradients, Percoll gradients, Sephadex columns, all subsequently resulting in unconfirmed sperm cell separation after DNA analysis and inconsistent gender report. Although a few of these mean differences are real on a population basis, the differences are so small that it is currently impossible to measure most of them in sufficient accuracy in individual sperm (Garner and Seidel, 2008). Therefore, we can easily say that sperm cells are essentially identical in size, weight, electrical charge, swimming speed, and most other variables. Not much time had to pass though, and the first live birth of mammals by sex preselection through X- and Y-separation by DNA and cell sorting, was reported thanks to a breakthrough regarding the DNA staining when using the membrane permeant bisbenzimidazole fluorescent dye, Hoechst 33342 that would stain DNA in intact sperm cells (Johnson et al., 1989). Such method still represents the only currently recognizable, viable and consistent manner to distinguish between living X- and Y- bearing spermatozoa due to the difference in their total DNA content and to the larger size of the X chromosome (Pinkel et al., 1982; Figure 2). Following the birth of the first sexed rabbits, pregnancies and birth have been reported in swine (Johnson, 1991), ovine (Morrell and Dresser, 1989), and bovine (Cran et al., 1993).

More attempts, in the course of the intervening years, have lengthened the list of species with viable offspring produced by the use of sexed semen. The first successful separation of human X- and Y- bearing spermatozoa based on the 2.8% total DNA content difference using flow cytometry was reported by Johnson et al., (1993) and substantiated by fluorescence in situ hybridization (FISH) analysis by Vidal et al., (1998), whereas the first deliveries of normal babies after use of flow cytometric separated human sperm cells was reported in 1998 by Fugger et al. Offspring from a variety of other species in addition to the ones earlier noted, have been reported over the years like horses (Buchanan et al., 2000; Lindsey et al., 2002), elk (Schenk and DeGrofft, 2003), cats (Holt et al., 2007), dogs (Meyers et al., 2008), dolphins (O'Brien et al., 2006) and non human primates (O'Brien et al., 2003).

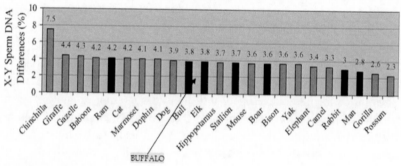

Garner, 2006 modified.

Figure 2. DNA content in X- and Y- bearing spermatozoa in various species.

4. METHOD FOR SPERM SORTING

The method currently in use, relies on the flow cytometric separation of X- and Y- bearing spermatozoa, by exploiting the intrinsic different DNA content between the two sperm cell populations. As seen in Figure 3, prior to flow cytometric sorting, semen is labelled with the fluorescent dye Hoechst 33342, which binds to the DNA of each spermatozoon. As the X chromosome is larger and therefore has more DNA content than the Y chromosome, the "female" (X-chromosome bearing) spermatozoa will absorb a greater amount of dye than its male (Y-chromosome bearing) counterpart. As a consequence, when exposed to UV light during flow cytometry, X spermatozoa fluoresce brighter than Y- spermatozoa. As the spermatozoa pass through the flow cytometer in single file, each spermatozoon is encased by a single droplet of fluid and assigned an electric charge corresponding to its chromosome status (eg X-positive charge, Y-negative charge). The stream of X- and Y- droplets is then separated by means of electrostatic deflection and collected into separate collection tubes for subsequent processing. While highly accurate, sperm sorting by flow cytometry will not produce two completely separate sperm cell populations. In fact, we should describe more appropriately a sample of sorted spermatozoa, as an "enriched" X- or Y-sperm population. The development of more sophisticated and efficient instruments for high speed flow cytometry was linked to the ability to orient the sperm cell so that DNA content could be measured through exposure of the flat side of the sperm head. The exact percentage purity of each population is dependent on the species being sorted and the 'gates' which the operator places around the total population visible to the machine. In general, the larger the DNA difference between the X and Y chromosome of a species the easier it is to produce a highly pure population. In sheep and cattle, purities for each sex will usually remain above 90% depending on 'gating', while for humans these may be reduced to 90% and 70% for "female" and "male" spermatozoa, respectively (Seidel and Garner, 2002).

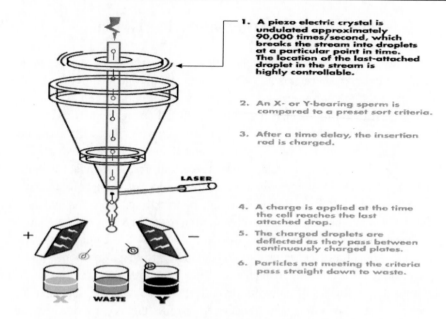

1. A piezo electric crystal is undulated approximately 90,000 times/second, which breaks the stream into droplets at a particular point in time. The location of the last-attached droplet in the stream is highly controllable.

2. An X- or Y-bearing sperm is compared to a preset sort criteria.

3. After a time delay, the insertion rod is charged.

4. A charge is applied at the time the cell reaches the last attached drop.

5. The charged droplets are deflected as they pass between continuously charged plates.

6. Particles not meeting the criteria pass straight down to waste.

Figure 3. Schematic representation of semen sorting by flow cytometry.

Furthermore, within the same species, i.e. cattle, differences in the differential amount of DNA content between X- and Y-bearing spermatozoa exist (Figure 4). Therefore, for buffalo spermatozoa, as it is for large ruminants and other species as well, the sequence of events leading to selected sperm cell population can be summarized in the following: 1. Sperm cells stained with fluorescent dye enter sorter; 2. A piezo electric crystal undulates, which breaks the stream into ~90,000 droplets/second; 3. A laser beams blue light on sperm cells; 4. X-chromosome-bearing sperm cells fluoresce with 4% more intensity than Y-chromosome-bearing sperm; 5. A computer processes the fluorescence detected and categorizes the sperm as X, Y or uncertain; 6. Negative, positive or no charge is applied to droplets depending on the intensity of sperm cell fluorescence and therefore of sex; 7. The charged droplets are deflected as they pass between continuously charged plates; 8. Sperm cells are collected in three containers, as X-, Y-chromosome-bearing and unsorted. Although some mechanical damage is unavoidable to the sperm cells while being sorted, this can be lowered by reducing the fluidic pressure from 50 to 40 psi (Suh et al., 2005). Sperm cell viability and stability of sperm DNA during and following the sex sorting procedure though, is not compromised as evidenced by a lack of significant damage to the sperm cell chromatin during the procedure itself. Damage to the sperm cells through the entire process is likely not to be addressed to the genetic content, but to be limited to some functional aspects in the ability to fertilize the mature oocytes. (Garner and Suh, 2002). Since the year 2000 there have been no major advances or breakthroughs in the technology itself, although some advances have been made resulting in a more efficient sperm sexing procedure. Such improvements can be identified into two major areas of investigation, namely: i) increase in the number of sperm cells being sexed per unit of time, and ii) reducing the damage to the sperm cells making them more viable through for example the optimization of the flow cytometer pressure (Seidel, 2007).

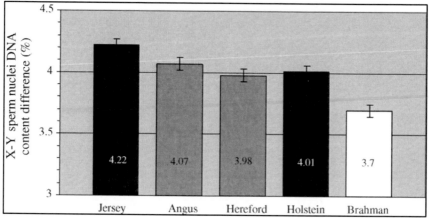

Garner, 2006.

Figure 4. Breed difference in cattle between X and Y bearing spermatozoa DNA content.

The capacity to effectively select the wanted sperm cell population depends on a number of variables of which the: i) measurement resolution, ii) the fluidic orientation and optical techniques, iii) the statistics and timing aspects, and iiii) cell orientation together with conformation and size of the sperm cell head are probably the most important. With regard to the sperm cell, yield and throughput in flow sorting depend largely on orientation of the cell arising from the paddled shape of the sperm head in most mammalian species (Figure 5). In fact, whenever sperm cells present themselves mostly by their edge toward the excitation source, it results in an inadequate illumination in order to provide a clear X or Y resolution (Sharpe et al., 2008).

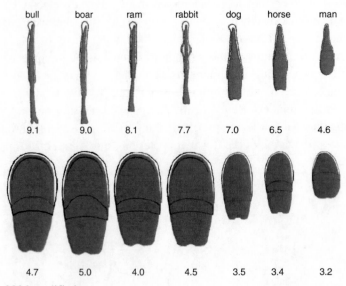

Garner, 2006 modified.

Figure 5. Front and lateral view with size (µm) of sperm cells from different species.

5. BUFFALO SEX CHROMOSOMES

The first step leading to the birth of viable calves following use of sexed semen can be identified in the study carried out on the detection of buffalo sex chromosomes in spermatozoa by fluorescence in situ hybridization (FISH). Revay et al., (2003, Figure 6) used some X- and Y-specific probe set derived from flow sorted yak chromosomes which labelled in somatic metaphases of water buffalo the whole X and Y, respectively, with the exception of the centromere regions. This study showed the possibility to use such yak probes to assess reliably separation of X- and Y-bearing spermatozoa, and demonstrated the evolutionary conservation of this locus in the water buffalo. Hence, the efficacy of sperm separation procedure and purity validation of sorted samples can be determined on a sample aliquot either by reanalysis (Welch and Johnson, 1999), by PCR (Welch et al., 1995) or else by using FISH techniques with X- and Y-chromosome specific probes to stain individual spermatozoa (Revay et al., 2003).

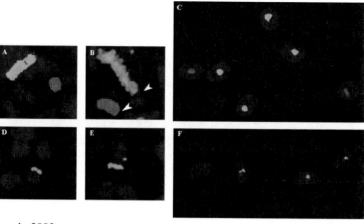

Revay et al., 2003.

Figure 6. Yak X and Y specific paint set through FISH on cattle (a) and water buffalo (b) sex-chromosomes, and water buffalo spermatozoa (c). X-chromosomes are detected in green and Y-chromosomes in red. Arrowheads indicate the unlabelled centromeres of the water buffalo gonosomes. In the second row (d–f), the Y-chromosome is labelled with the BC1.2 probe on chromosomes and cells as above.

6. AI BY USING SEXED SEMEN

6.1. Herd Management and Synchronization Protocols

The use of AI in buffaloes has always been hampered in the past by poor results and efficiency. Protocols for synchronization of estrus, typically employed in cattle with sufficient proficiency were not the right move to obtain similar wanted results in buffaloes. In fact, in comparison to cattle, buffaloes are characterized by a much wider variation of the timing involved among the various steps leading to ovulation, especially when exogenous hormonal control is applied to the animals for synchronization of estrus. As a consequence, such aspects make the implementation of estrous protocols more problematic in comparison to cattle. Some major differences exist between cattle and buffaloes with regard to the time interval between estrus and ovulation, whereas in cattle, the time interval separating the LH surge, the beginning of behavioral estrus and ovulation is usually quite consistent and uniform. In buffaloes, on the contrary, such interval is far wider and accompanied by a much reduced frequency and intensity of behavioral estrus

(Presicce, 2007). Therefore, even the use of simple protocols involving correct prostaglandin administration at the right interval, may produce a wide variability in the timing of ovulation among the synchronized animals (Zicarelli et al., 1988). In addition, estrous synchronization protocols rely on the clear evidence of estrous signs both within the target animals than among animals themselves, in order to have them subjected to insemination at the correct time, and to obtain the highest pregnancy rate. Unfortunately in buffaloes, the well known poor intensity of estrous signs and homesexual behaviour make the protocols for synchronization of estrus much less reliable in comparison to cattle (Presicce et al., 2007). Recently though, the advent and implementation of protocols for synchronization of ovulation in cattle has paved the road for a wider and more efficient utilization of AI in buffaloes. Since the first described protocol for synchronization of ovulation (Pursley et al., 1995), some modifications have been adopted for heifers and cows and nowadays a large variety of modification to the original protocol are used worldwide. Synchronization of ovulation has given immediately good and consistent results in both heifers and pluriparous buffaloes. Since then, modifications to the Ovsynch protocol have been tested when applied to buffaloes too, with continuing satisfying results in synchronization of the ovulation process and in pregnancy rates following AI similar to what usually reported in cattle (Neglia et al., 2003; De Rensis et al., 2005). The optimization of synchronization protocols for ovulation and consistency in pregnancy rates was instrumental in the acceptance by farmers of such an important tool for the reproductive management of buffaloes, leading to intensity of selection and increased speed of yearly genetic gain. The achievement of satisfying pregnancy rates when using AI in buffaloes, made possible the development of a strategy to use AI in conjunction to frozen / thawed sexed semen.

6.2. Buffalo Sexed Semen

In a preliminary seminal study prior to the use of sexed semen in buffaloes, a specific device was tested for artificial semen deposition near the utero-tubal junction (Ghent device) in order to deliver a significant reduced concentration of semen, in comparison with a conventional concentration deposited in the body of the uterus. It was shown that a dose of 4×10^6 sperm cells deposited near the utero-tubal junction could bring a pregnancy rate similar to what achieved with an ordinary concentration of 20×10^6 sperm cells into the body of the uterus (Presicce et al., 2004). These satisfying results brought to the next step, where, for the very first time, semen was collected in the year 2004 from a 2 year old buffalo bull (named "Sbirulino") in a farm in the South of Italy and shipped overnight to a collaborating laboratory in Germany. In such laboratory, the semen was sexed and the procedure used enabled sperm cell populations to be selectively sorted and enriched with a purity similar to what reported for cattle bulls (Figure 7).

In this very first trial involving the use of frozen thawed buffalo sexed semen, pluriparous buffaloes were made available and synchronized by a standard Ovsynch protocol. A collaborating group developed a specific AI gun characterized by an inner and more flexible segment enveloped by an outer and more rigid cover (Ghent device). Such set up enabled the operator to pass through the cervical barrier into the proximal portion of the uterine horn ipsilateral to the ovary bearing the ovulatory follicle. At that point, the inner segment of the AI gun would be gently pushed forward up to the utero-tubal junction and guided by the hand transrectally. This methodology would allow the deposition of reduced number of sperm cells as high as possible into the reproductive tract optimizing as much as possible their availability for fertilization (Figure 8).

The semen was then frozen and shipped back to Italy for AI using the Ghent device, as described by Presicce et al., (2004), obtaining pregnancy rates similar to the use of non-sexed semen at much higher concentration (Presicce et al., 2005a). The first buffalo calves born following use of AI and sexed semen in the world, showed at birth a normalcy in all parameters usually assessed under ordinary postnatal care (Presicce et al., 2005b). Following these first encouraging results, the impact and feasibility of flow cytometric sorting of X- and Y- sperm cells of Murrah and Nili-Ravi buffalo bulls have been studied (Lu et al., 2006), leading to the born of the first buffalo calves produced by the combined use of in vitro fertilization procedures (IVF) and sexed semen (Lu et al., 2007), showing that this new approach in the toolbox of reproductive technologies, can be used to efficiently exploit valuable sorted semen. The possibility to retrieve immature oocytes from preantral follicles in large ruminants by means of transvaginal guided puncture or ovum pick up (OPU), has open new possibilities for genetic improvement within herds and breeding schemes (Pieterse et al., 1991). Although the efficiency of late stage in vitro embryo production in buffaloes, following OPU and IVF can be considered similar to what reported in cattle (Neglia et al., 2003b), the development to term following transfer of fresh or frozen embryos is still unsatisfactory (Neglia et al., 2003c; Lu et al., 2007). Nevertheless, the combined use of IVF, OPU and sexed semen has been proven feasible and repeatable, mushrooming new research for a wider field application of these technologies in buffalo (Liang et al., 2008).

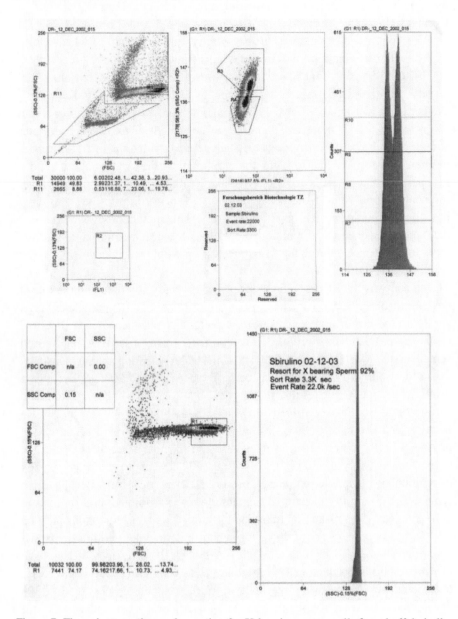

Figure 7. Flow chart: sorting and resorting for X-bearing sperm cells from buffalo bull.

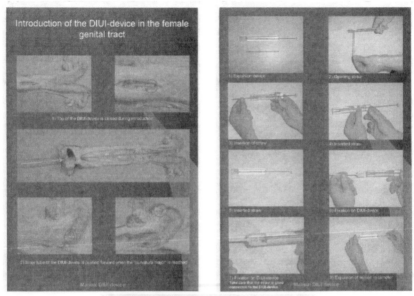

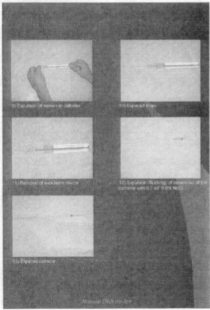

Figure 8. Use of Ghent device (see text) and correct procedure for depositing small amount of sexed semen at the utero-tubal junction.

Table 1. Timetable of events related to sexing semen technology in buffaloes and available literature

	*Buffalo Type	X-Y Sperm/AI IVF	** X 10^6	Journal	Year
Revay et al.,	Mediterranean	X-Y FISH	-	Reprod. Dom. Anim.	2003
Presicce et al.,	Mediterranean	AI	4	Reprod. Dom. Anim.	2005
Lu et al.,	Murrah/Nili Ravi	X-Y sorting		Anim. Reprod. Sci.	2006
Lu et al.	Murrah/Nili Ravi	IVF	1-2/ml	Anim. Reprod. Sci.	2007
Liang et al.,	Murrah/Nili Ravi	IVF	1-2/ml	Theriogenology	2008
Lu et al.,	Murrah/Nili Ravi	AI	2	Anim. Reprod. Sci.	2010
Campanile et al.,	Mediterranean heifers	AI	2	Theriogenology	2011
Campanile et al.,	Mediterranean pluriparous	AI	2	Theriogenology	2013

*semen source; ** million of spermatozoa per dose (AI) or mL (IVF).

More recently, very high pregnancy rates following AI with buffalo river type sexed semen into swamp and F1 (River x Swamp) recipients undergoing spontaneous estrus, have been reported (Lu et al., 2010). These last successful results indicate a powerful way to disseminate valuable semen for the acceleration of genetic gain in swamp buffalo too, bearing in mind the different breeding management and local conditions typical of Asian Countries. The first large trial on the use of sexed semen in Mediterranean buffalo heifers has confirmed the similarity of efficiency and pregnancy rates when compared to the use of conventional semen (Campanile et al., 2011). In this study, a modified Presynch-Ovsynch protocol for synchronization of ovulation was implemented. Additional variation within the protocol consisted of an adjunctive administration of GnRH and prostaglandin at the time of AI, in order to verify the beneficial combined effect on possible synchronous ovulation and enhanced internal progesterone production. In the same study, it has been shown that sexed semen deposition into the body of the uterus gives similar pregnancy rates if compared to the deep semen deposition into the uterine horn. This latter finding will facilitate the dissemination and use of sexed semen, since no special skills or particular technique, as seen in Presicce et al., (2005b), are necessary to obtain acceptable pregnancy rates. More recently, on a similar trial on pluriparous buffaloes subjected to AI with sexed semen during the seasonal and transitional breeding periods, a conventional Ovsynch protocol was employed, reducing thus manpower on handling of animals and reducing the need of exogenous hormonal administration, and at the same time reporting good conception rates non dissimilar from the use of conventional semen (Campanile, 2013). See Table 1 for a chronological order of events related to the study and implementation of the sexed semen technology in the buffalo species.

7. SEXED SEMEN AND IVF

The use of advanced reproductive technologies in buffaloes, like in vitro embryo production procedures, has mushroomed over the past decade highlighting successes and pitfalls (Gasparrini et al., 2002). Protocols for IVF adjusted and optimized in cattle have been adopted in buffaloes, and later reconciled with the need of new adjustments for some species-specific differences (Gasparrini et al., 2005). The reasons for an increased interest in the utilization of IVF protocols in buffaloes has to be linked to the fact that in vivo embryo production in buffaloes has never been very efficacious since the very early attempts (Schallenberger et al., 1990; Baruselli et al., 1999) and in the intervening years up to date. The reasons considered to be causative of a reduced efficiency in embryo production were thought to be found initially in a lower response to exogenous hormonal stimulation, and later to anatomically enlarged ovaries due to the presence of high number of ovulatory follicles leading to an inadequate capacity of oviductal fimbriae to capture oocytes (Baruselli et al., 2000). The adoption of in vitro embryo production technology in the buffalo species has been seen then, as the only possibility to use elite superior females in conjunction to semen from superior bulls. Nowadays, efficiency in the production of in vitro embryos can be considered consistent and efficient and to a very large extent similar to production efficiency reported in cattle. Production of embryos through in vitro technology in buffaloes likewise cattle, benefits from the possibility to recover oocytes from live animals through ultrasound assisted puncture of antral follicles, both in prepuberal as well as in pluriparous animals (Presicce et al., 2007). Recently, following the very early reports of successful and consistent conception rates in buffaloes after use of sexed semen and AI (Presicce et al., 2005a), preselected sperm cells have been included in protocols for in vitro embryo production procedures with encouraging results non dissimilar from the use of conventional unsexed semen when considering late stage embryo development rates and birth of calves at term (Liang et al., 2008). It is conceivable that, with advancing progress in the activation protocols of buffalo oocytes, sexed sperm cells will be even more part of integrated assisted reproductive technologies, with particular reference to the injection of single sperm cell into the oocyte cytoplasm. This additional advance will contribute to the reduction of calves of unwanted gender, and consequential more resourceful and efficient farm management.

8. NORMALCY OF CALVES BORN FROM THE USE OF SEXED SEMEN

From the available literature, it seems that cattle calves born following use of sexed / frozen-thawed semen show that gestation length, neonatal death, calving difficulty, birth weight, weaning weight, or live births are similar to births derived from the use of unsexed frozen/thawed sperm (Tubman et al., 2004). Although embryonic blastomeres, as seen following IVF procedures, retain some of the Hoechst 33342 dye usually up to the 16-cell stage and occasionally up to 32- to 128- cell stage, the genetic impact on the developmental competence of such embryos can be considered negligible (Tubman et al., 2004). Nevertheless, some contrasting data have been presented on the same issue, reporting a somewhat inferior or delayed development of embryos derived from the use of sperm sex selection when compared to the adoption of conventional unsorted semen (Wilson et al., 2005). Conclusively, to date more than a million mammalian offspring have been produced following Hoechst 33342-staining of sperm cells and sex sorting, with no reports of abnormal phenotypes in the offspring derived in cattle (Morrell and Dresser, 1989). This is substantiated by an absence of DNA damage to sperm DNA due to staining with Hoechst 33342 followed by intense laser light exposure in the course of the sorting process. More importantly, the wavelengths of laser light used are not absorbed by DNA or proteins, thus minimizing potential damage (Garner and Seidel, 2008). It seems that in dairy cattle, female calves produced by the use of sexed semen result in lower weight at birth, lowering thus the incidence of dystocia (Tubman et al., 2004). In buffaloes, viability and related parameters of calves born following use of sexed semen via AI were evaluated and compared to calves born following use of non sexed semen. In such study, weight of calves following parturition, ease of delivery and postnatal respiratory distress were monitored and found similar between the two groups of buffalo calves (Presicce et al., 2005b). Normalcy in all parameters considered were confirmed in a more recent study on calves born both within the breeding season as well as during the transition period (Campanile et al., 2013).

9. ECONOMIC IMPLICATIONS

As highlighted above, sorted sperm cells have resulted in pregnancies in a number of species, farm animals and humans. Pre-selecting the sex of animals used for production in agriculture is particularly valuable in instances where one sex is more valuable within the production chain. For example, in commercial dairy operations with the exception of a few bull calves produced from the very top cows, male calves have little value. On the other hand, the value of heifer calves is at a premium. The opposite is true in commercial beef cattle production. Sperm cell sorting would allow commercial dairy and beef producers to select semen that when used, would produce the desired sex in a majority of the animals. This technology would also benefit producers using crossbreeding systems that employ maternal (F-1cows) and/or terminal cross lines because only a minimum number of cows would be needed to produce crossbred replacements or slaughter animals depending on production goals. To give an example in the dairy cattle industry, some research has shown that F-1 *Bos taurus* X *Bos indicus* females are considered to be the most productive in the Gulf Coast region of the United States. One of the major deterrents to producing *Bos taurus* X *Bos Indicus* replacement females is how to successfully market the male counterparts. Sexed semen would not only reduce the number of purebred cows needed to produce the heifers, but very few males would be produced almost eliminating the need to market this class of animal. In buffaloes, historically in the Mediterranean Region and in Italy in particular where this species is considered of great economic importance, male calves have always been considered an unwanted offspring and a burden for the farmers; with the exception of retaining a few of them derived from the best female producers of the herd. In fact, in most buffalo farms still today, natural mating is the preferred choice and an average of 1 bull to 15 to 25 females is a rule-of-thumb used for an optimal male to female ratio within the herd. The use of sexed semen in those farms that have decided to rely on the adoption of AI within their herds, may change significantly the scenario. In fact, if we consider a typical buffalo farm in Italy, with: i) an average herd milk production of around 2,550 kg per lactation, ii) a 20% animal turnover due to a longer longevity of production animals in this species, iii) assuming a 0% mortality within the herd and iiii) the need to produce 20 replacement heifers, we will have the possibility to use only the 50 best female buffaloes for AI with sexed semen (around 50% pregnancy and slightly reduced final birth rate) vs the use of the 90 best female buffaloes for AI with conventional unsexed semen (where half of born calves will be males). The genetic contribution to milk increase when using sexed semen and a reduced number of the top producing females will be then roughly 5 times higher when compared to the use of conventional semen (Table 2).

Table 2. Genetic contribution to increase in milk production when using sexed vs non sexed semen in an average producing buffalo farm

Turnover coefficient 20%; calf mortality = 0; average milk production in the herd = kg 2.550		
	semen	
	sexed	non sexed
To get	20	20
Conception %	40	45
Best % buffaloes to AI	50	90 (*)
Average milk production (kg)	2800	2600
Selective differential (kg)	250	50
Hereditability (30%)	75	15
* Half will be males		

Zicarelli, unpublished.

Reducing thus, almost by half the number of the top producers of the herd to be inseminated when using sexed semen, in less than a decade an average increase in milk production per animal of around 200 kg is to be expected translating into an increased income of 250 Euro per animal, even when considering the higher cost of sexed semen in comparison to conventional non sexed semen (Zicarelli, unpublished). Collectively, it can be concluded that the use of sexed semen into intensive buffalo breeding both improves the reproductive management within farms, as well as the net income to farmers derived from milk production of each animal.

REFERENCES

[1]   Abdou, M.S.S., El Sayed, M.A.I., Seida, A.A., & El Wishy, A.B. (1982). Gonadal and epididymal sperm numbers in adult buffulo bulls. *Vet. Med. J. Giza*, 30, pp. 327.

[2]   Amann, RP, & Seidel, GE. Prospects for sexing mammalian sperm. *Animal Reproduction Laboratory, Fort Collins*, Colorado, USA, 1982.

[3]   Arrighi, S., Bosi, G., Groppetti, D. & Cremonesi, F. (2010). Morpho- and histometric evaluations on the testis and epididymis in buffalo bulls during the different reproductive seasons. *The Open Anatomy Journal*, 2, pp. 29-33.

[4]   Baruselli PS, Madureira EH, Visintin JA, Porto-Filho R, Carvalho NAT, Campanile G, Zicarelli L. Failure of oocyte entry into oviduct in superovulated buffalo. *Theriogenology* 2000;53:491.

[5]   Baruselli PS, Mucciolo RG, Arruda R, Madureira EH, Amaral R, Assumpcao MEOA. Embryo recovery rate in superovulated buffalo. *Theriogenology* 1999;51:401.

[6]   Boccia, L., Di Palo, R., De Rosa, A., Attanasio, L., Mariotti, E., Gasparrini B. (2007). Evaluation of buffalo semen by Trypan blue/Giemsa staining and related fertility in vitro. *Italian Journal of Animal Science*, 6, 2, pp. 739-742, ISSN: 1594-4077.

[7]   Bongso, T.A., Hassan, M.D., & Nordin, W. (1984). Relationship of scrotal circumference and testicular volume to age and body weight in Swamp buffalo. *Theriogenolog* , 22, pp. 127–134.

[8]   Buchanan BR, Seidel Jr GE, McCue PM, Schenck JL, Herickhoff LA, Squires EL. Insemination of mares with low numbers of either unsexed or sexed spermatozoa. *Theriogenology* 2000;53:1333-44.

[9] Campanile G, Gasparrini B, Vecchio D, Neglia G, Senatore EM, Bella A, Presicce GA, Zicarelli L. Pregnancy rates following AI with sexed semen in Mediterranean Italian buffalo heifers. *Theriogenology* 2011;76:500-06.

[10] Campanile G, Vecchio D, Neglia G, Bella A, Prandi A, Senatore EM, Gasparrini B, Presicce GA. Effect of Season, Late Embryonic Mortality and Progesterone Production on Pregnancy Rates in Pluriparous Buffaloes (*Bubalus bubalis*) Following Artificial Insemination with Sexed Semen. *Theriogenology* 2012 accepted for publication.

[11] Cran DG, Johnson LA, Miller NGA, Cochrane D, Polge C. Production of bovine calves following separation of X- and Y-chromosome bearing sperm and in vitro fertilization. *Vet Rec* 1993;132:40-51.

[12] De Rensis F, Ronci G, Guarneri P, Nguyen BX, Presicce GA, Huszenicza G, Scaramuzzi RJ. Conception rate after fixed time insemination following ovsynch protocol with and without progesterone supplementation in cyclic and non- cyclic Mediterranean Italian buffaloes (Bubalus bubalis). *Theriogenology* 2005;63:1824–1831.

[13] El-Azab, A.I., Rakha, A.M., & Farag, Y.A. (1978). A direct estimate of gonadal and extra-gonadal sperm reserves in the buffalo bull. *Egyptian J. Vet. Sci.*, 15, pp. 9.

[14] El-Azab, A.I. (1980). The interaction of season and nutrition on semen quality in buffalo bulls. Ph. D. Thesis, Cairo University, 1980.

[15] El-Sheltawi, M., Adbel Malak, G., Abdel-Rahman, A. & Abdou, M.S.S. (1995). Can cold shock test predict the freezability of buffalo spermatozoa. *Proc. 7th Annual Congr. Egypt. Soc. Anim. Reprod. Fert.*, Cairo, Egypt, 1995, pp. 279.

[16] Fugger EF, Black SH, Keyvanfar K, Schulman JD. Births of normal daughters after MicroSort sperm separation and intrauterine insemination, in vitro fertilization, or intracytoplasmic sperm injection. *Hum Reprod* 1998;13:2367–2370.

[17] Garner DL, Seidel Jr GE. History of commercializing sexed semen for cattle. *Theriogenology* 2008;69:886-95.

[18] Garner DL, Suh TK. Effect of Hoechst 33342 staining and laser illumination on viability of sex-sorted bovine sperm. *Theriogenology* 2002;57:746.

[19] Garner DL. Flow cytometric sexing of mammalian sperm. *Theriogenology* 2006;65:943-57.

[20] Gasparrini B, Neglia G, Di Palo R, Campanile G, Zicarelli L. Effect of cysteamine during in vitro maturation on buffalo embryo development. *Theriogenology* 2000;54:1537–1542.

[21] Gasparrini B. In vitro embryo production in buffalo species: state of the art. *Theriogenology* 2002;57:237–256.

[22] Holt WV, O'Brien J, Abaigar T. Applications and interpretation of computer-assisted sperm analyses and sperm sorting methods in assisted breeding and comparative research. *Reprod Fertil Devel* 2007;19:709-19.

[23] Ibrahim, R.A. (1985). Seasonal changes in sperm production of buffalo bulls. *M.V.Sc thesis*, Cairo University, 1985.

[24] Johnson LA, Flook JP, Hawk HW. Sex preselection in rabbits: live births from X and Y sperm separated by DNA and cell sorting. *Biol Reprod* 1989;41:199–203.

[25] Johnson LA, Welch GR, Keyvanfar K, Dorfmann A, Fugger EF, Schulman JD. Gender preselection in humans? Flow cytometric separation of X and Y spermatozoa for the prevention of X-linked diseases. *Hum Reprod* 1993;8:1733-9.

[26] Johnson LA. Sex preselection in swine: altered sex ratios in offspring following surgical insemination of flow sorted X- or Y- bearing sperm. *Reprod Dom Anim* 1991;26:309-14.

[27] Kiddy, CA & Hafs, HD. Sex ratio at birth – Prospects for control. *Am Soc Anim Sci.* Champaign, USA, 1971.

[28] Kumar, S., Sahni, K.L. & Bistha, G.S. (1993). Cytomorphological characteristics of motile and static semen of buffalo bulls. *Buffalo Journal*, 2, pp. 117–127.

[29] Liang XW, Lu YQ, Chen MT, Zhang XF, Lu SS, Zhang M, Pang CY, Huang FX, Lu KH. In vitro embryo production in buffalo (Bubalus bubalis) using sexed sperm and oocytes from ovum pick up. *Theriogenology*. 2008 Apr 15;69(7):822-6. Epub 2008 Mar 11.

[30] Lindsey AC, Schenck JL, Graham JK, Bruemmer JE, Squires EL. Hysteroscopic insemination of low numbers of flow sorted fresh and frozen/thawed stallion spermatozoa. *Equine Vet J* 2002;34:121-7.

[31] Lu Y, Zhang M, Lu S, Xu D, Huang W, Meng B, Xu H, Lu K. *Anim Reprod Sci*. 2010 Jun;119(3-4):169-71. Epub 2010 Jan 14.

[32] Lu YQ, Liang XW, Zhang M, Wang WL, Kitiyanant Y, Lu SS, Meng B, Lu KH. Birth of twins after in vitro fertilization with flow-cytometric sorted buffalo (Bubalus bubalis) sperm. *Anim Reprod Sci.* 2007 Jul;100(1-2):192-6. Epub 2006 Sep 15.

[33] Lu YQ, Wang WL, Yang H, Liang XW, Liang YY, Zhang M, Lu SS, Kitiyanant Y, Lu KH. Flow-cytometric sorting the sperm and production of sex-preselected embryo in buffalo (Bubalus bubalis). Proceedings of the 5th Asian Buffalo Congress, Nanning, China, 18–22 April, 2006:155– 161.

[34] Meyers MA, Burns G, Arn D, Schenck JL. Birth of canine offspring following insemination of a bitch with flow-sorted spermatozoa. *Reprod Fertil devel* 2008;20:213.

[35] Mirabella, N., Squillacioti, C., De Luca, A. & Paino, G. (2007). Seasonal reproductive activity and innervation of vas deferens and accessory male genital glands in the Water buffalo (*Bubalus bubalis*). *Ital J Anim Sci*, 6, pp. 636-639.

[36] Morrell JM, Dresser DW. Offspring from inseminations with mammalian sperm stained with Hoechst 33342, either with or without flow cytometry. *Mutat Res* 1989;224:177-83.

[37] Neglia G, Gasparrini B, Caracciolo di Brienza V, Di Palo R, Campanile G, Presicce GA, Zicarelli L. Bovine and buffalo in vitro embryo production using oocytes derived from abattoir ovaries or collected by transvaginal follicle aspiration. *Theriogenology* 2003b;59:1123–1130.

[38] Neglia G, Gasparrini B, Caracciolo di Brienza V, Di Palo R, Campanile G, Zicarelli L. First pregnancies estab- lished from vitrified blastocysts entirely produced in vitro in Mediterranean Italian buffalo cows. *Theriogenology* 2003c;59:374.

[39] Neglia G, Gasparrini B, Di Palo R, De Rosa C, Zicarelli L, Campanile G. Comparison of pregnancy rates with two oestrus synchronization protocols in Italian Mediterranean Buffalo cows. *Theriogenology* 2003a;60:125–133.

[40] O'Brien JK, Hollingshead FKI, Evans KM, Evans G, Maxwell WMC. Flow cytometric sorting of frozen-thawed spermatozoa in sheep and non-human primates. *Reprod Fertil Dev* 2003;15:367-75.

[41] O'Brien JK, Robeck TR. Development of sperm sexing and associated assisted reproductive technology for sex preselection of captive bottlenose dolphins (*Tursiops truncatus*). *Reprod Fertil Devel* 2006;18:319-29.

[42] Pant, H.C., Sharma, R.K., Patel, S.H., Shukla, H.R., Mittal, A.K., Kasiraj, R., Misra, A.K., & Prabhakar, J.H. (2003). Testicular development and its relationship to semen production in Murrah buffalo bulls. *Theriogenology*, 60, pp. 27–34.

[43] Perera, B.M. (1999). Reproduction in water buffalo: comparative aspects and implications for management. *J Reprod Fertil Suppl*, 54, pp. 157–168.

[44] Pieterse MC, Vos PLAM, Kruip ThAM, Wirth YA, van Beneden ThH, Willemse AH, Taverne MAM. Transvaginal ultrasound guided follicular aspiration of bovine oocytes. *Theriogenology* 1991;35:19–24.

[45] Pinkel D, Gledhill BL, Lake S, Stephenson D, Van Dilla MA. Sex preselection in mammals? Separation of sperm bearing Y and "O" chromosomes in the vole *Microtus oregoni*. *Science* 1982;218:904-5.

[46] Presicce GA, Rath D, Klinc P, Senatore EM, Pascale M. Buffalo calves born following AI with sexed semen. *Reprod Domest Anim* 2005b;40:349.

[47] Presicce GA, Verberckmoes S, Senatore EM, Jeroen Dewulf J, Van Soom A. Assessment of a new utero-tubal junction insemination device in the Mediterranean Italian water buffalo (Bubalus bubalis) under field conditions. Bubalus bubalis ISSN:1594-7718 2004;58-64.

[48] Presicce GA, Verberckmoes S, Senatore EM, Rath D. First established pregnancies in Mediterranean Italian buffaloes (Bubalus bubalis) following deposition of sexed spermatozoa near the utero tubal junction. Reprod Domest Anim 2005a;40:73–75.

[49] Presicce GA. Reproduction in the Water Buffalo. *Reprod Dom Anim* 2007;42:24-32.

[50] Presicce, G.A., Revay, T., Nagy, S.Z., Dinnyes, A. & Kovacs, A. (2003). Complex staining of water buffalo (*Bubalus bubalis*) spermatozoa. *Bubalus bubalis*, 2, pp. 55–60.

[51] Pursley JR, Mee MO, Wiltbank MC. Synchronization of ovulation in dairy cows using PGF2a and GnRH. *Theriogenology* 1995;44:915–923.

[52] Rana, B.K., & Bilaspuri, G.S. (2000). Changes in interstitial cells during development of buffalo testis. *The Veterinary Journal*, 159, pp. 179-185.

[53] Rath D, Moench-Tegeder G, Taylor U, Johnson LA. Improved quality of sex-sorted sperm: a prerequisite for commercial application. *Theriogenology* 2009;71:22-29.

[54] Révay T, Kovacs A, Presicce GA, Rens W, Gustavsson I. Detection of water buffalo sex chromosomes in spermatozoa by fluorescence *in situ* hybridization. *Reprod Dom Anim* 2003;38:377-9.

[55] Saeed, A., Chaudhry, R.A., Khan, I.H. & Khan, N.U. (1990). Morphology of semen buffalo bulls of different age groups. In: Acharya RM, Lokeshwar RR, Kumar S (eds), *Recent Advances in Buffalo Research,* Vol. 3, pp. 17-19, International Development Research Centre, New Delhi, India.

[56] Sansone, G., Nastri, M.J.F. & Fabbrocini, A. (2000). Storage of buffalo *(Bubalus bubalis)* semen. *Anim Reprod Sci,* 62, pp. 55–76.

[57] Schallenberger E, Wagner HG, Papa R, Hartl P, Tenhumberg H. Endocrinological evaluation of the induction of superovulation with PMSG in water buffalo (Bubalus bubalis). *Theriogenology* 1990;34:379-92.

[58] Schenck JL, DeGrofft DL. Insemination of cow elk with sexed frozen sperm. *Theriogenology* 2003;39:514.

[59] Seidel Jr GE, Garner DL. Current status of sexing mammalian sperm. *Reproduction* 2002;24:733-43.

[60] Seidel Jr GE. Overview of sexing sperm. Theriogenology 2007;68:443-6.

[61] Seren, E., & Parmeggiani, A. (1997). Oestrus cycle in Italian buffalo. *Bubalus bubalis,* IV/97 (suppl), pp. 21-28.

[62] Sharpe JC, Evans KM. Cell analysis apparatus and methods, United States Patent PCT/US08/73915. 2008.

[63] Suh TK, Dchenk JL, Seidel Jr GE. High pressure flow cytometric sorting damages sperm. *Theriogenology* 2005;64;1035-48.

[64] Tubman LM, Brink Z, Suh TK, Seidel Jr GE. Characteristics of calves produced with sperm sexed by flow cytometry. *J Anim Sci* 2004;53:1029–36.

[65] Vale, W.G., Gastal, D.W., Snel-Oliveira, M.V., & Mondadori, R.G. (2001). Relationship of age, bodyweight and scrotal circumference in Murrah buffalo bulls. *Proc.of the 6th World Buffalo Congress,* Maracaibo, Venezuela, May 2001, pp. 256-262.

[66] Vidal F, Fugger EF, Blanco J, Keyvanfar K, Catala V, Norton M, et al. Efficiency of Microsort flow cytometry for producing sperm populations enriched in X- or Y-chromosome haplotypes: a blind trial assessed by double and triple colour fluorescent in-situ hybridization. *Hum Reprod* 1998;13:308-12.

[67] Wilson RD, Weigel KA, Fricke PM, Rutledge JJ, Leibfried-Rutledge ML, Matthews DL. In vitro production of Holstein embryos using sexsorted sperm and oocytes from selected cull cows. *J Dairy Sci* 2005;88:776-82.

[68] Ziada, M.S., Abdel-Malak, G., & Abdou, M.S.S. (1992). Effect of glycerol concentration and thawing regimes on the viability of frozen buffulo spermatozoa. *Proc. 4ᵗʰ Annual Congr.* Egypt. Soc. Anim. Reprod. Fert., Cairo, Egypt, 1992, pp. 133.

[69] Ziada, M.S., Adbel Malak, G., El-Sheltawi, M., & Ismail T.I.M. (1995). Studies on frozen buffalo semen: Effect of bulls, diluents and thawing rates. *Proc. 7ᵗʰ Annual Congr. Egypt. Soc. Anim. Reprod. Fert.*, Cairo, Egypt, 1995, pp. 265.

[70] Zicarelli L, Infascelli F, Esposito L, Consalvo F, De Franciscis G. Influence of climate on spontaneous and alfapr- ostol induced heats in Mediterranean buffalo cows bred in Italy. Proceedings of the Second World Buffalo Congress, New Delhi, India, vol. III, 1988:49–56.

[71] Zicarelli, L. (1997). Reproductive seasonality in buffalo. *Proceedings of the Third Course on Biotechnology of Reproduction in Buffaloes* (Issue II), Caserta, Italy, October, 1997, pp. 29–52.

In: Advances in Reproductive Technology ...   ISBN: 978-1-62417-875-7
Editor: Ignatz Sanger   © 2013 Nova Science Publishers, Inc.

Chapter 4

ASSISTED REPRODUCTIVE TECHNOLOGIES AND RISK FOR AUTISM SPECTRUM DISORDER

Ditza A. Zachor[a] and Esther Ben-Itzchak[b]

[a]Assaf Harofeh Medical Center, Tel Aviv University
[b]Ariel University Center, Israel

ABSTRACT

The current estimated prevalence of autism spectrum disorder (ASD) is approximately 1:100-150, which reflects a 15-fold increase from studies published a half-century ago. The exact cause of ASD is still unknown and it is now believed that, despite the strong genetic origin, environmental factors may modulate phenotypical expression. Pre-and perinatal events are now the focus of research into risk factors for ASD. Assisted reproductive technology (ART) now accounts for 1-3% of all live births in the western world. Several procedures that may be used in the ART process, such as hormonal stimulation, egg retrieval, *in vitro* fertilization (IVF), intra-cytoplasmic sperm injection (ICSI), micro-manipulation of gametes and exposure to culture medium, could subject the gametes and early embryos to environmental stress. Although these techniques are considered safe, in recent years evidence has been accumulating that ART may be associated with an increased risk of birth defects, low birth weight (LBW), and genetic imprinting disorders. Children arising from ART are also at higher risk for epigenetic and imprinted disorders. Epigenetics refers to heritable modifications of DNA that do not alter the underlying sequence. DNA methylation and histone modification are examples of epigenetic modifications that may lead to imprinting disorders. The majority of evidence regarding the effect of ART on imprinting involves DNA methylation. A possible association between the increase in ART procedures and the increase in ASD prevalence has been investigated. Previous studies have reported conflicting results concerning the association between assisted conception and the risk for ASD. This chapter will address the recent literature on the association between the use of hormonal induction and/or assisted reproductive technologies and the risk for autism. Possible contributing mechanisms will be discussed.

INTRODUCTION

Autism spectrum disorders (ASD) are a group of neurobehavioral disorders defined by social and communication deficits and repetitive and stereotyped behaviors. ASD comprise a spectrum delineated by a set of observable dysfunctions with wide variability with respect to the presence and intensity of the core symptoms and cognitive and language skills [1]. The current estimated prevalence of ASD is approximately 1% [2], which reflects a 15-fold increase from studies published a half-century ago. Although the increased prevalence may be associated, to some degree, with alterations in definitions and with improved diagnostic ability, it is believed that at least some of the increase in prevalence reflects a real change.

ASD are biologically-based disorders, although the exact etiology is still unknown. While ASD have a very significant genetic basis with inheritability of 60-90%, (reviewed in Schaaf & Zoghbi, 2011) [3], genetic factors alone cannot provide an explanation for the increased prevalence. The incomplete concordance in monozygotic twins, the fact that the exact cause of ASD is still unknown, and the acceleration in ASD rates in recent years suggests that non-heritable environmental factors might increase the risk for ASD [4, 5].

BIRTH RISK FACTORS FOR AUTISM SPECTRUM DISORDERS

Symptoms of autism can be identified as early as in the first two years of life. Moreover, studies have pointed to brain abnormalities that suggested the relevant period of the occurring insults in ASD may be *in utero* (reviewed in

Amaralet al., 2008) [6, 7]. Therefore, birth events that are more frequent in this epoch are now the focus of research into risk factors for ASD, especially in light of the increased prevalence of ASD in recent years. No individual factor in the neonatal and perinatal periods has been consistently validated as a risk factor for autism. However, some pre-and perinatal events that have been associated with ASD in several previous studies might provide a small contribution to the etiology of ASD. Among the birth risk factors for ASD, family factors include advanced maternal and paternal ages, primiparous women, and having a mother born outside of Europe, North America or Australia (reviewed in Gardner's meta-analysis, 2009) [8]. Regarding pregnancy-related risk factors, bleeding and using medication, especially psychiatric, during the pregnancy have been associated with ASD. During the perinatal period, the predominant risk factors were preterm birth, breech presentation and Caesarian section. In the neonatal period, risk factors associated with ASD were low birth weight, low Apgar scores and hyperbilirubinemia (reviewed in Guinchat et al., 2012) [9].

ASSISTED CONCEPTION

One major transformation in the field of obstetrics is the new options for assisting in fertilization using assisted reproductive technologies (ART). Assisted conception includes the use of ovulation-inducing drugs, *in vitro* fertilization (IVF), and intra-cytoplasmic sperm injection (ICSI) [10-12]. Ovulation-inducing drugs (OID), such as clomiphene citrate, follicle-stimulating hormone (FSH) and human chorionic gonadotropin (HCG), have often been the first line of treatment in infertility [10]. IVF and ICSI procedures have been increasingly used during the last 30 years and now account for approximately 1-4% of live births in the western world [13]. The use of OID, egg retrieval, micro-manipulation of gametes and exposure to the culture medium could subject the gametes and early embryos to environmental stress that may lead to aberrant developmental outcomes.

Although these techniques are considered safe, in recent years evidence that assisted conception may be associated with abnormal outcome has been accumulating. One of the major reported adverse outcomes is the increased risk of birth defects after assisted conception [14-16]. A recent large study documented high rates of birth defects (8.3% vs. 5.8% in natural conception). When looking at the type of assisted conception used, only the use of the ICSI procedure was associated with this increased rate of birth defects [14]. This study suggested that the type of assisted conception affected outcome. In addition, assisted conception has been associated with genetic aberrations, including chromosomal anomalies[17] and genetic imprinting disorders [15-20]. Moreover, high rates of low birth weight (LBW), neurological abnormalities [21], cerebral palsy [13, 22] and developmental delay [23, 24] were reported after assisted conception as well. However, it is important to note that results are inconsistent. Of the OID used in infertility, only clomiphene citrate was associated with an increased risk of birth defects [14, 25].

ASSISTED CONCEPTION AND RISK FOR ASD

Assisted conception and ASD share several risk factors. In both, high rates of advanced parental ages [26, 27], hormonal disturbances especially in testosterone/androgen regulation [28, 29], high rate of preterm deliveries and low birth weight [26, 30-31] have been reported. Given the previous findings, the increased prevalence of both ASD and ART in recent years might be related.

Previous studies reported conflicting results concerning the association between assisted conception and ASD [32-40] (Table 1). Several studies reported more cases of ASD in the population that underwent IVF procedures, but results lacked statistical significance [32, 37-39]. One study reported significant increased risk for a broad range of psychiatric disorders, including ASD [33] in ART pregnancies. An Israeli study during 1970-1998, using a case-control cohort of ASD population in residential placement, found a high obstetric and neonatal sub-optimality score that included assisted conception [34]. Hvidtjorn et al. (2011) [35] reported that children born after assisted conception had an increased risk of ASD diagnosis. However, the risk disappeared when data was adjusted for other risk factors (maternal age, educational level, parity, multiplicity, and smoking). Only a subgroup of women who received follicle stimulation hormone (FSH) in addition to IVF treatment had a stable increased risk for ASD. In contrast, one study reported a protective effect of assisted conception and risk of ASD [36]. Several other studies reported that IVF is not a significant risk factor for ASD [37, 38]. Shimada et al. (2012) [40] attempted to explore whether an association exists between assisted reproductive technology (IVF and ICSI) and ASD in a Japanese population using a retrospective chart review during the years 2006-2009. The researchers compared the frequencies of ART in three disorders, ASD, attention deficit hyperactivity disorder (ADHD) and Tourette syndrome

(TS). In cases where the presence or absence of ART could be ascertained (ASD n = 467; ADHD n = 64; TS n = 83), the rate of ART in cases of persons with ASD (4.5%) was 1.8 times the frequency expected in the general population, while ART was not present in cases of persons with ADHD and TS. The authors reported that the ASD cases had a significantly higher parental age which is considered a risk factor for ASD as well.

Most of the above described studies originated from population-based research in the Scandinavian countries, which are very similar in demographic and ethnicity factors. Therefore, it is difficult to over-generalize these findings to other populations with different ethnic profiles. Most of these studies obtained information on outcome from hospital discharge registers [32, 33, 36-40] and were not based on a standardized assessment of ASD. Studies that assessed assisted conception as a risk factor for ASD differed in the selection of outcome measures of ASD, as some used infantile autism, some ASD, and one applied an even broader range of psychiatric diagnoses including ASD. The definition of ASD differed among studies, as some used ICD-10 and others DSM III–IV criteria. Most studies covered populations between 1982 and 2001, and only one recent study covered up to 2003 [35]. Therefore, most studies used outdated criteria for ASD, which might underestimate the number of ASD cases. Regarding the relation between ovulation induction and higher risk for ASD, a recent nested case-control study within the Nurses' Health Study (n=116,430) found no significant association between self-reported fertility therapies or history of infertility and a diagnosis of ASD. In subgroup analyses, women with maternal age ≥35 years who had artificial insemination had significantly higher rates of ASD. Ovulation induction drugs (OID) were significantly associated with ASD in crude but not adjusted analyses. In addition, within the advanced maternal age group, OID and artificial insemination were significantly associated with Asperger syndrome and pervasive developmental disorder not otherwise specified (PDD-NOS), but not with autistic disorder [41].

In a case-control research, Zachor & Ben-Itzchak (2011) [42] reported a significantly higher prevalence of assisted reproductive technologies (IVF and ICSI) (10.7%) among a large clinic-based well-characterized ASD population in comparison to the rate of ART (3.06%) in a large Israeli population. All the children were diagnosed based on standardized 'gold standard' tests. In this study, parental age distribution did not differ in the two ASD groups, with and without assisted conception. Since ART procedures are considered for infertile couples who are usually older, after attempts to conceive spontaneously failed, it was important to assess the impact of maternal and paternal ages on the risk for ASD versus the direct effect of the ART. Maternal age was significantly advanced in both ASD groups (with and without ART) in comparison to the general population. However, the age distribution in both ASD groups, with and without ART, did not differ, suggesting that the ART group was not specifically older. The frequency of ART in the young maternal age range (mothers younger than 29 years) within the ASD group was still significantly higher (8.7%) than the average rate of ART in the Israeli population (3.06%). This high rate of ART in young mothers suggested that ART may be an independent risk factor for ASD in this group.

Previous studies documented that several obstetric conditions appeared to increase the risk of autism (prematurity, low birth weight). Similarly, assisted conception (IVF, ICSI) was associated with adverse perinatal outcome such as prematurity and low birth weight because of the strong association between IVF and ICSI and multiple pregnancies and because even IVF singletons have an increased risk of prematurity and low birth weight compared with naturally conceived singletons[43]. To assess whether the effects of these birth risk factors were related to the increased risk for ASD, Zachor & Ben-Itzchak (2011) excluded twin pregnancies from their entire ASD group. The singleton ASD with assisted conception group had similar rates of prematurity and low birth weight in comparison to the general population [42]. These findings suggested that assisted conception may be an important risk factor for ASD, but is not associated with other established risk factors which may play a role in those without ART.

Regarding a history of ASD in the family, none of the ASD with ART group and 14.7% in the ASD without ART group had a relative with ASD, suggesting less genetic susceptibility in the ASD with ART group.

Finally, the 2011 Zachor & Ben Itzchak study addressed a very important topic, whether the use of ART was associated with unique autism symptomatology that might represent a distinct clinical phenotype in this group. Different aspects of the clinical presentation of ASD were examined, including autism severity, adaptive functioning, and history of developmental regression, in both the ASD with and without ART groups [42]. The clinical presentation in those two ASD subgroups was not significantly different, suggesting that the ART procedure might contribute to the risk for ASD but was not related to a unique clinical profile.

POSSIBLE CAUSAL MECHANISMS

Several mechanisms may link assisted conception to risk for ASD. One possibility may stem from conditions that relate to parental infertility, such as parental hormonal disturbances that may require ART. Hormonal abnormalities could link assisted conception to ASD, as some cases of infertility may be hormonal-related and hormonal medications are used in fertility treatment protocols. Several theories have tried to explain the link between abnormal sex hormones and ASD. First, increased fetal testosterone level was described in children with ASD [28]. Second, women diagnosed with ASD have a significantly greater prevalence of polycystic ovary syndrome, delayed puberty and abnormal menstrual cycles in adulthood in comparison to controls [44]. Third, children diagnosed with ASD have lower levels of FSH and higher serum levels of total testosterone [29].

Another possible mechanism may involve epigenetic changes that have been linked to the use of ART [19, 20]. Epigenetics is the study of heritable changes in gene expression or cellular phenotype caused by mechanisms other than changes in the underlying DNA sequence. Epigenetics typically involves stable silencing/activating of a gene or a gene regulatory element. The variety of molecules involved in gene silencing and the requirement for active maintenance of epigenetic states creates a potential for errors on a large scale. Such errors, leading to misexpression of a gene, may cause diseases. The stochastic and reversible nature of epigenetic phenomena predicts that epigenetic mutations are likely to be mosaic and inherited in a non-Mendelian manner and may display variable expressivity and complex patterns of inheritance. Much phenotypic variation and common disease might be explained by epigenetic variation and aberration. Moreover, as epigenetic changes (unlike DNA changes) need to be maintained, they may be influenced by variable factors including environmental factors such as diet, providing a disease mechanism that involves both inherited and environmental factors. Evidence is accumulating, for example, that dietary factors can modify epigenetic markers. Hence, in some cases, effects of an altered dietary supply of methyl donors on DNA methylation may affect methylation, leading to gene expression changes and phenotypical changes [45]. However, while epigenetics is suspected to be involved in many pathologic processes, the known examples of true epigenetic disease are limited at present [46].

Table 1. Studies on assisted conception and risk of ASD.

Source	Country	Design/ASD diagnosis	Association with ASD
Shimada et al, 2012 [40]	Japan 2006-09	Chart review	ART in ASD >general population >> ADHD or TS
Zachor & Ben Itzchak, 2011 [42]	Israel	Case-control ASD cohort, diagnosed by standardized tests, 2001-10	In ASD cohort: ART in ASD group - 10.7% vs 3.06% in the general population
Hvidtjon et al, 2010 [35]	Denmark 1995-2003	Population-based ICD-10	High risk for ASD - unadjusted NS - Adjusted to maternal age and parity High risk for ASD: IVF+FSH
Knoester et al, 2007 [23]	Netherlands 2004-05	Case-control	>ASD cases
Maimburg, 2007 [36]	Denmark 1990-99	Case-control ICD-10	NS Low risk - protective
Stein et al, 2006 [34]	Israel 1970-98	Case-control ASD population DSM-III-IV	High obstetric and neonatal suboptimality score
Klemetti et al, 2006 [33]	Finland 1996-99	Retrospective cohort ICD-10	>ASD cases
Lidegaard et al, 2005 [37]	Denmark 1995-2001	Retrospective cohort (singletons) ICD-10	NS
Pinborg et al, 2003 [32]	Denmark 1995-2001	Retrospective cohort (twins) ICD-10	>ASD/Asperger cases
Ericson et al, 2002 =[39]	Sweden 1984-97	Retrospective cohort ICD-10	>ASD cases
Stromberg et al, 2002 [38]	Sweden 1982-95	Retrospective cohort ICD-10	NS

The first evidence of association between ART and aberrant imprinting was provided in 2000 [19], involving two newborns with Angelman syndrome, the prototype of epigenetic disorders, born after ART. Molecular analysis detected sporadic imprinting defects in both patients. A larger prospective study showed that ART is associated with a human overgrowth syndrome, Beckwith-Wiedemann syndrome (BWS), another example of an imprinting disorder. The study found that BWS was about six times more prevalent

(4.6%) in cases of ART compared with the general rate in the United States (0.8%). The study showed, again, that these cases were associated with sporadic epigenetic changes, specifically with aberrant methylation [47].

How epigenetic changes can explain increased risk for ASD in ART is an important question. Parental infertility may be related to epigenetic changes in the gametes leading to both the infertile state requiring ART and ASD. Another possible mechanism is that the ART procedure itself is related to a risk for ASD. Exposure to high hormonal doses for ovulation induction, the use of various test-tube materials or the vitamin and amino acids content of the media may all lead to epigenetic changes.

Given these results, the increased prevalence of both ASD and ART in recent years might be related. Of all the known assisted conception procedures, ICSI has been specifically related to birth defects and, therefore, may be the main candidate for the association with the increased risk of ASD. As imprinting alterations were proved to be associated with ART and with specific disease processes, it is important to explore whether assisted conception is related to an increased risk for ASD and to molecular alterations such as imprinting changes.

REFERENCES

[1]   Johnson CP, Myers SM (2007) American Academy of Pediatrics Council on Children with Disabilities. Identification and evaluation of children with autism spectrum disorders. *Pediatrics* 120:1183-1215.

[2]   Kogan MD, Blumberg SJ, Schieve LA, Boyle CA, Perrin JM, Ghandour RM, Singh GK, Strickland BB, Trevathan E, van Dyck PC (2009) Prevalence of parent-reported diagnosis of autism spectrum disorder among children in the US. *Pediatrics* 124:1395-1403.

[3]   Schaaf CP, Zoghbi HY (2011) Solving the autism puzzle a few pieces at a time. *Neuron* 70:806-8.

[4]   Veenstra-VanderWeele J, Cook EH (2004) Molecular genetics of autism spectrum disorder. *Molecular Psychiatry* 9:819–32.

[5]   Klauck SM (2006) Genetics of autism *European Journal of Human Genetics* 14:714-20.

[6]   Amaral DG, Schumann CM, Nordahl CW (2008) Neuroanatomy of autism. *Trends in Neuroscience* 31:137-45.

[7]   Anagnostou E, Taylor MJ (2011) Review of neuroimaging in autism spectrum disorders: what have we learned and where we go from here. *Molecular Autism* 2:4.

[8]   Gardener H, Spiegelman D, Buka SL (2009) Prenatal risk factors for autism: comprehensive meta-analysis. *British Journal of Psychiatry* 195:7–14.

[9]   Guinchat V, Thorsen P, Laurent C, Cans C, Bodeau N, Cohen D (2012) Pre-, peri- and neonatal risk factors for autism. *Acta Obstetricia et Gynecologia Scandinavia* 91:287–300.

[10]   Homburg R, Insler V (2002) Ovulation induction in perspective. *Human Reproduction Update* 8:449–62.

[11]   Andersen AN, Goossens V, Gianaroli L, Felberbaum R, de Mouzon J, Nygren KG. (2007) Assisted reproductive technology in Europe, 2003: Results generated from European registers by ESHRE. *Human Reproduction* 22:1513-25.

[12]   Wright VC, Chang J, Jeng G, Chen M, Macaluso M; Centers for Disease Control and Prevention (2007) Assisted reproductive technology surveillance: United States, (2004). *MMWR Surveillance Summary* 56:1-22.

[13]   Hvidtjørn D, Schieve L, Schendel D, Jacobsson B, Sværke C, Thorsen P (2009) Cerebral palsy, autism spectrum disorders, and developmental delay in children born after assisted conception. A systematic review and meta-analysis. *Archives of Pediatrics and Adolescents Medicine* 163:72-83.

[14]   Davies MJ, Moore VM, Willson KJ, Van Essen P, Priest K, Scott H, Haan EA, Chan A (2012) Reproductive technologies and the risk of birth defects. *The New England Journal of Medicine* 366:1803-13.

[15]   Hansen M, Kurinczuk JJ, Bower C, Webb S (2002) The risk of major birth defects after intracytoplasmatic sperm injection and in vitro fertilization. *The New England Journal of Medicine* 346:725–30.

[16]   Merlob P, Sapir O, Sulkes J, Fisch B (2005) The prevalence of major congenital malformations during two periods of time, 1986-1994 and 1995-2002, in newborns conceived by assisted reproduction technology. *European Journal of Medical Genetics* 48:5–11.

[17]   Bonduelle M, Van Assche E, Joris H, Keymolen K, Devroey P, Van Steirteghem A, Liebaers L (2002) Prenatal testing in ICSI pregnancies: incidence of chromosomal anomalies in 1586 karyotypes and relation to sperm parameters. *Human Reproduction* 17:2600-14.

[18] Gosden R, Trasler J, Lucifero D, Faddy M (2003) Rare congenital disorders, imprinting genes, and assisted reproductive technology. *Lancet* 361:1975-7.

[19] Cox GF, Bürger J, Lip V, Mau UA, Sperling K, Wu BL, Horsthemke B (2002) Intracytoplasmic sperm injection may increase the risk of imprinting defects. *American Journal of Human Genetics* 71:162-4.

[20] Lidegaard O, Pinborg A, Andersen AN (2006) Imprinting disorders after assisted reproductive technologies. *Current Opinion in Obstetrics & Gynecology* 18:293-6.

[21] Schieve LA, Meikle SF, Ferre C, Peterson HB, Jeng G, Wilcox LS (2002) Low and very low birth weight in infants conceived with use of assisted reproductive technology. *The New England Journal of Medicine* 346:731-6.

[22] Källén B, Finnström O, Nygren KG, Olausson PO (2005) In vitro fertilization in Sweden: child morbidity including cancer risk. *Fertility and Sterility* 84:605-10.

[23] Knoester M, Helmerhorst FM, van der Westerlaken LA, Walther FJ, Veen S (2007) Matched follow-up study of 5 8-year-old ICSI singletons: child behavior, parenting stress and child (health-related) quality of life. *Human Reproduction* 22:3098-107.

[24] Ito A, Honma Y, Inamori E, Yada Y, Momoi MY, Nakamura Y (2006) Developmental outcome of very low birth weight *Journal of Perinatology* 26:130-3.

[25] Reefhuis J, Honein MA, Schieve LA, Rasmussen SA; National Birth Defects Prevention Study (2011). Use of clomiphene citrate and birth defects, National Birth Defects Prevention Study, 1997-2005. *Human Reproduction* 26:451-7.

[26] Ben Itzchak E, Lahat E, Zachor DA (2011) Advanced parental ages and low birth weight in autism spectrum disorders – rates and effect on functioning. *Research in Developmental Disability* 32:1776-81.

[27] Hultman CM, Sandin S, SZ, Lichtenstein P, Reichenberg A (2011) Advancing paternal age and risk of autism: new evidence from a population-based study and a meta-analysis of epidemiological studies. *Molecular Psychiatry* 16:1203–12.

[28] Auyeung B, Baron-Cohen S, Ashwin E, Knickmeyer R, Taylor K, Hackett G (2009) Fetal testosterone and autistic traits. *British Journal of Psychology* 100:1-22.

[29] Geier DA, Geier MR (2006) A clinical and laboratory evaluation of methionine cycletranssulfuration and androgen pathway markers in children with autistic disorders. *Hormonal Research* 66:182-8.

[30] Larsson HJ, Eaton WW, Madsen KM, Vestergaard M, Olesen AV, Agerbo E, Schendel D, Thorsen P, Mortensen PB (2005) Risk factors for autism: perinatal factors, parental psychiatric history, and socioeconomic status. *American Journal of Epidemiology* 161:916-25.

[31] Mann JR, McDermott S, Bao H, Hardin J, Gregg A (2010) Pre-eclampsia, birth weight, and autism spectrum disorders. *Journal of Autism and Developmental Disorders* 40:548–54.

[32] Pinborg A, Loft A, Schmidt L, Andersen AN (2003) Morbidity in a Danish national cohort of 472 IVF/ICSI twins, 1132 non-IVF/ICSI twins and 634 IVF/ICSI singletons: health-related and social implications for the children and their families. *Human Reproduction* 18:1234-43.

[33] Klemetti R, Sevon T, Gissler M, Hemminki E (2006) Health of children born as a result of in vitro fertilization. *Pediatrics* 118:1819-27.

[34] Stein D, Weizman A, Ring A, Barak Y (2006) Obstetric complications in individuals diagnosed with autism and in healthy controls. *Comprehensive Psychiatry* 47: 69-75.

[35] Hvidtjørn D, Grove J, Schendel D, Schieve L, Sværke C, Ernst E, Thorsen P (2010) Risk of autism spectrum disorders in children born after assisted conception: a population-based follow-up study. *Journal of Epidemiology and Community Health* 65:497-502.

[36] Maimburg RD, Vaeth M (2007) Do children born after assisted conception have less risk of developing infantile autism? *Human Reproduction* 22:1841-3.

[37] Lidegaard O, Pinborg A, Andersen AN (2005) Imprinting diseases and IVF: Danish National IVF cohort study. *Human Reproduction* 4:950-4.

[38] Strömberg B, Dahlquist G, Ericson A, Finnström O, Köster M, Stjernqvist K (2002) Neurological sequelae in children born after in-vitro fertilization: a population based study. *Lancet* 359:461-5.

[39] Ericson A, Nygren KG, Olausson PO, Kallen B(2002) Hospital care utilization of infants born after IVF. *Human Reproduction* 17:929-32.

[40] Shimada T, Kitamoto A, Todokoro A, Ishii-Takahashi A, Kuwabara H, Kim S-Y, Watanabe K, Minowa I, Someya T, Ohtsu T, Osuga Y, Kano Y, Kasai K, Kato N, Sasaki T (2012) Parental age. *Research in Autism Spectrum Disorder* 6:500-7.

[41] Lyall K, Pauls DL, Spiegelman D, Susan L, Santangelo SL, Ascherio A (2012) Fertility therapies, infertility and autism spectrum disorders in the Nurses' Health Study II. *Paediatric and Perinatal Epidemiology* 26:361–72.

[42] Zachor DA, Ben Itzchak E (2011) Assisted reproductive technology *Research in Developmental Disabilities* 32:2950-6.

[43] Helmerhorst FM, Perquin DA, Donker D, Keirse MJ (2004) Perinatal outcome of singletons and twins after assisted conception: a systematic review of controlled studies. *British Medical Journal* 328:261.

[44] Ingudomnukul E, Baron-Cohen S, Wheelwright S, Knickmeyer R (2007) Elevated rates of testosterone-related disorders in women with autism spectrum conditions. *Hormones & Behavior* 51:597-604.

[45] McKay JA, Wong YK, Relton CL, Ford D, Mathers JC (2011) Maternal folate supply and sex influence gene-specific DNA methylation in the fetal gut. *Molecular Nutrition & Food Research* 11:1717-23.

[46] Martin DI, Cropley JE, Suter CM (2011) Epigenetics in disease: leader or follower? *Epigenetics* 6: 843-8.

[47] DeBaun MR, Niemitz EL, Feinberg AP (2003) Association of in vitro *American Journal of Human Genetics* 72:156-60.

INDEX

congenital malformations, viii, 2, 33, 35, 37,
    38, 39, 41, 42, 43, 44, 46, 47, 48, 49, 50,
    54, 57, 58, 64, 66, 150
Congress, 136, 138, 139
conservation, xi, 111, 122
containers, 120
controlled studies, 63, 68, 153
controversial, 91, 93
corpus luteum, 91
correlation coefficient, 76, 84, 85
correlation(s), 76, 77, 84, 85, 100
cost, 30, 69, 133
counseling, x, 52, 73, 78
covering, ix, 32, 72
crown, 76, 100, 106
culture, vii, xii, 30, 65, 141, 143
culture conditions, 30
culture medium, vii, xii, 141, 143
cycles, 69
cytometry, 118, 119, 120, 136, 138
cytoplasm, 130

damages, 138
data analysis, 60
data collection, 26, 33, 51, 58
data set, 66
database, 32, 33, 51, 66
deaths, 53, 64, 91
defects, vii, viii, ix, xii, 2, 4, 31, 32, 33, 34,
    35, 39, 40, 41, 44, 45, 47, 49, 51, 52, 53,
    54, 55, 56, 57, 58, 59, 62, 63, 64, 65, 66,
    67, 68, 69, 70, 74, 97, 141, 143, 148,
    149, 150, 151
deficiencies, 58
deficit, 144
demographic data, 34
demography, 68
Denmark, 84, 102, 148
deposition, xi, 112, 124, 125, 129, 137
depression, 69
depth, 117
detection, ix, x, xi, 71, 72, 73, 83, 85, 87,
    90, 97, 99, 101, 105, 108, 111, 116, 122

developed countries, ix, 3, 4, 71, 81
developmental disorder, 145
diabetes, x, 73
diaphragmatic hernia, 39, 44, 58, 68
diet, 147
dietary supply, 147
discordance, 64, 68
diseases, ix, 2, 34, 35, 55, 135, 147, 152
disorder, vii, x, xii, 73, 80, 89, 141, 144,
    145, 148, 149
distress, 131
distribution, 12, 16, 27, 76, 86, 101, 116,
    145
dizygotic, 3, 10, 23, 32, 54, 59, 61, 64
dizygotic twins, 10, 32, 54, 61
DNA, xii, 97, 99, 101, 106, 108, 117, 118,
    119, 120, 121, 130, 135, 141, 147, 153
DNA damage, 130
DNA sequencing, 99, 106, 108
dogs, 118
donors, 147
Down syndrome, 98, 100, 103, 104, 105,
    106, 107, 108, 109, 110
drugs, 143, 145
DSM, 145
ductus arteriosus, 37, 42, 46, 48, 50, 54

egg, vii, xii, 7, 141, 143
egg retrieval, vii, xii, 141, 143
Egypt, 134, 139
ejaculation, 115
electric charge, 119
elk, 118, 138
encouragement, xi, 112
endocrine, 113
England, 61, 62, 101
environmental effects, 58
environmental factors, xii, 141, 142, 147
environmental stress, xii, 141, 143
enzymes, 116
epidemiologic, 4, 23, 31, 32, 63
epidemiologic studies, 31
epidemiology, 61

T

U

V